THE
FACILITIES
MANAGER'S
REFERENCE

R.S. Means Company, Inc.

THE FACILITIES MANAGER'S REFERENCE

Management

Planning

Building Audits

Estimating

Harvey H. Kaiser, Ph.D.

R.S. MEANS COMPANY, INC.
CONSTRUCTION CONSULTANTS & PUBLiSHERS
100 Construction Plaza
P.O. Box 800
Kingston, MA 02364-0800
(617) 585-7880

This book was edited by Gregory Magee, Melville Mossman, and Julia Willard. Typesetting was supervised by
Helen Marcella. The book and jacket were designed by Norman Forgit.

Printed in the United States of America

10 9 8 7 6 5 4 3 2

Library of Congress Catalog Card Number 89-189303
ISBN 0-87629-142-6

Dedication

This book is dedicated to my children, Sven-Erik, Robert, and Christina. Their contribution to this book is the time they sacrificed while their father was distracted by the ideas and labors that evolved into its completion.

TABLE OF CONTENTS

FOREWORD

Coordinating an organization's resources to allow for optimum working efficiency is the focus of facilities management, whether the facility is a single building, institution, industrial plant, office complex, or worldwide enterprise. For a facility to sufficiently maintain its standards for current use and accommodate new uses, the individual managing the facility must thoroughly comprehend the business structure and operating framework of the organization. The willingness to take action and make decisions are key traits the facilities manager must possess to effectively perform the dual role of advisor to senior management and supervisor of staff.

The dual roles of the facilities manager's position may seem to differ substantially and it is often a wonder that they can be grouped together under one entity at all. However, since the main objective is effective management of *all* capital assets, then the facilities manager must oversee not only the buildings that make up the organization's main capital assets, but also the personnel who ensure the availability, usefulness, and extended life cycle of these buildings. Facilities management is the governing entity supervising property management, facilities planning, operations and maintenance, and facilities support service functions.

Suggested by the two very different facilities management roles of advisor and supervisor, this book is divided into two parts. The first part, "Principles of Facilities Management," is devoted to explaining management practices for the various departments within facilities management. Since determining annual capital needs is one of the main tasks of the facilities manager, Part II describes a system for evaluating the existing conditions of a facility. This system—the Facilities Audit—is a means of identifying deficiencies that will lead to capital projects, estimating the cost of each individual project, and then totalling these costs to arrive at an overall annual capital budget allowance.

This book is written for managers who have the authority and fiscal responsibility for making facilities-related decisions, as well as owner's representatives or facilities managers with line responsibilities and roles in policy-advising and staff supervision. Additionally, this book is invaluable to senior officers with overall facilities responsibilities, and line managers whose positions may lead them towards advancement to positions of facilities managers. Architects, engineers, interior designers, and vendors of supplies and equipment, who provide support services to facilities management, will also benefit from this information. Finally, students in facilities management-related areas will find the text to be of assistance in developing an understanding of the field and potential future responsibilities.

Acknowledgments

Many of the concepts and examples of facilities management contained in this book were developed through the author's experience as an administrator at Syracuse University. The author would like to thank the following staff members for being especially tolerant of working and contributing to the refinement of these ideas: John Sala, Director of Physical Plant; Virginia Denton, Director of Design and Construction; John Zrebiec, Director of Security; and Michael Riley, Director of Support Services, and his administrative assistant, Elizabeth Volan, for patiently editing and managing the preparation of many earlier drafts of this material.

Colleagues in the management of physical plants across the country also added to the development of the material through comments based on their experiences. Especially helpful were staff members of the Association of Physical Plant Administrators of Colleges and Universities (APPA). Walter Schaw, Wayne LeRoy, Steven Glazner, and other staff members provided assistance through comments and observations on the "state of the art." The Facilities Audit section of this book was developed from ideas originally presented in the *Facilities Audit Workbook*, published by the APPA. Material used from APPA's *Facilities Management: A Manual for Plant Administrators* is also acknowledged where not specifically cited. The author would also like to mention the contributions of: H.C. Lott, William Middleton, William Gardiner, Jack Hug, Clinton Hewett, and Gene Cross.

Finally, the author expresses his appreciation to the staff of R.S. Means Company, Inc. for encouraging the development of this book from a collection of ideas and rough draft material. Ferol Breymann, Acquisitions Editor, provided early encouragement on the project. Greg Magee's many technical and editing comments added to the polishing of early drafts. And finally, without the tireless, proficient editing and gentle urging by Julia Willard, the book would not have reached its final form.

Part One

PRINCIPLES OF FACILITIES MANAGEMENT

What is facilities management? This section guides the reader through the basic functions of facilities management, describing each activity, organizational responsibilities, and relationships. Distinctions are made for differences in size, location, and amounts of space in outlining the scope of responsibility and organizational structures. Strategic facilities planning is presented as a comprehensive view of managing facilities by clearly identifying the components of strategic planning and operational management.

Chapter One

INTRODUCTION TO FACILITIES MANAGEMENT

Organizations have traditionally managed the buying, building, leasing, selling, planning, maintaining, and equipping of space, so why the emergence of a new field called **Facilities Management** and the title of **Facilities Manager**? This management field has emerged in response to a need for one entity in an organization to oversee all facilities functions previously controlled by independent departments.

Evolution of Facilities Management

The job formerly known by such titles as **Buildings and Grounds Superintendent** or **Director of Physical Plant** is now just one of the responsibilities of the facilities manager. The term, "facilities," includes buildings, grounds, utilities, and equipment, and typically represents a majority of an organization's capital assets. The facilities manager must oversee not only all physical facilities management functions, but also the capital assets of an organization.

Historically, the capital assets of an organization were managed by a financial officer. The financial officer advised on property decisions; supervised operations and maintenance activities; budgeted these functions; assisted in hiring architects, engineers, and space planners; and paid the bills for consultants, construction, heating, power, and cleaning.

In small organizations, an administrative staff carried out these tasks and the financial officer advised on matters involving corporate policy. Larger organizations with individual departments divided the responsibilities of construction, property management, and space planning.

Government agencies, corporations, and nonprofit institutions realized that managing these functions within traditional organizational structures was unsatisfactory. There was no individual or single group coordinating all facilities decisions. With accountability and a single source of responsibility as the goal, facilities management emerged to overcome the fragmented management of facilities.

3

Management Concerns

Management concerns, ranging from expansions or reductions in the size of a physical plant to the manner in which the quality of the workplace affects employee productivity, define new facilities responsibilities. Demands for greater technical expertise in planning and building space, and efficiency and economy in plant operations and maintenance, require specialized management skills. New technologies, innovative materials, and complex space demands contribute to the growth of facilities management as a dynamically new professional field, complete with professional societies, special academic programs, and a rapidly growing collection of literature.

Organization Changes

A number of changes in organizations during the past two decades have contributed to the shift from fragmented responsibility and decision-making for facilities to a centralized management concept. These changes have had far-reaching effects, exposing a void in the management of capital assets. The impact of change is visible across the country, throughout a variety of organizations. These changes, and their effects on organizational needs, are described below.

- **Existing Facilities:** Obsolete facilities need extensive renovations to meet new requirements or to correct the effects of deferred maintenance on aging facilities.
- **Space Demands:** Organizational functional activities have grown and are constantly changing. Flexible, adaptable space is necessary to accommodate these changes.
- **Geo/Demographics:** Regional shifts in population and markets have occurred, affecting organizational missions and operations, as well as evaluations of facilities utilization.
- **Structural Changes in the National Economy:** The national economy has shifted dramatically from a manufacturing to a service economy, causing space abandonment, space conversions, and new space requirements.
- **Asset Dynamics:** Inflation and changing tax structures create a need for rapid, coordinated facilities decisions. Acceleration in the delivery of renovated or new space is necessary to keep up with rapidly rising costs, changes in financing methods, and depreciation, all of which affect decisions on buying, selling, or building space.
- **Corporate and Institutional Reorganization:** Growth through acquisition rather than expansion, a recent trend, requires that facilities decisions be made on location, renewal, replacement, or divesting existing facilities.
- **Quality of the Environment:** There has been a call for workplace efficiency and safety to enhance employee productivity. Government mandates for workplace standards to avoid health hazards, provisions for accessibility, and protection from hazardous materials are other environmental questions to be considered.
- **New Technologies:** Rapid advances in telecommunications and computer technology have drastically altered the individual workplace. This development has increased demands for innovations in space design and equipment. Advance planning is necessary to allow flexibility and anticipate changes in the ways organizations function and transmit information.

- **Energy:** Recent concerns for energy conservation require new building design, construction materials, and energy management systems. Space utilization and building operations procedures are also being re-examined to determine possible energy-saving measures.

Facilities management and the new position of facilities manager came into being with the need to address these varied concerns.

Capital Asset Management

With the evolution of any new management field, there is often confusion about the definition of the job. The "space environment" industry may contribute to some of the differences of opinion about what the field of facilities management *is* and *is not*. Manufacturers of office equipment and furnishings, responding to new technologies and environmental concerns, promote facilities management as the effective use of the office environment. Although an important responsibility, there is a larger role that facilities managers play—managing capital assets. This duty includes coordinating the property management, planning, constructing, maintaining, and equipping functions of a facility.

Comprehensive Facilities Management

A hallmark of facilities management is comprehensiveness. Included in the definition of comprehensive facilities management are the planning, designing, constructing, and managing of facilities for every type of structure, ranging from office buildings to housing to infrastructure. It involves developing:

- Corporate facilities policies
- Long-range space forecasts
- Real estate management plans
- Space inventories
- Projects (from design through construction)
- Building operations and maintenance plans
- Furniture and equipment inventories
- Facilities support services (telecommunications, security, etc.)

Management Based on Facilities Needs

An organization cannot be static in delivering its products and services. Managing facilities must be viewed as dynamic in order to respond to change. A basic principle of facilities management is that all policies, practices, and procedures are guided by an organization's mission and available resources. In this way, specific facilities management functions evolve from the "business" of an organization. Organizational structures are built around quantity of space, functional activities, and employee productivity in providing a service or product.

Strategic Planning

Foreign competition, innovation in manufacturing or providing services, broad social and economic change, and a wide range of external conditions compel corporate boards and managers to seek evaluations in not only *how* they do business, but in *what* their business should be. Computerization, telecommunications, and "smart" buildings fill the air in the discussions of facilities, generating a realization that managing facilities is a comprehensive activity. For these reasons, private and nonprofit organizations are introducing strategic planning to plan future strategies, long range objectives, and integrated programs for achieving these objectives. Strategic planning is an important function of the facilities management organization. It is discussed in more detail in Chapter 7.

Integrated Planning

The traditional physical plant manager thinks in terms of operational plans: how to get the job done with short term specific thinking. However, planning must be integrated to fit with other parts of an organization to achieve the best results. The facilities manager involved in integrated strategic planning aims at determining:

- The basic **nature** and **concept** of an organization
- The overall direction or **strategy** for fulfilling that concept
- Plan **execution**

Patrick Below, in *The Executive Guide to Strategic Planning*, has described the **integrated planning process**, shown in Figure 1.1. This process incorporates three major elements:

1. The Strategic Plan
2. The Operational Plan
3. Results Management

In this process, the facilities manager is a senior member of the organization's planning team, reporting to the chief executive officer on the development of the strategic plan (see Chapter 7). The role changes in the operational plan by focusing on how to achieve the plan within a comprehensive facilities management structure. In results management, the facilities manager monitors the implementation and results of both the strategic and operational plans. In this context, property management, facilities planning, facilities operation and maintenance, and facilities support services are viewed as an extension of organizational strategic plans.

Control and Communication

Control and communication are important ingredients of successful facilities management. Comprehensive facilities management is based on an organizational structure that controls property management decisions, facilities support services, and facilities operations.

Integrated Planning Process

Strategic Plan	Operational Plan	Results Management
Organization Mission	Operational Analysis	Control Systems
Strategic Analysis	Key Results Areas	Management Reports
Strategy	Indicators of Performance	Organization Results
Long-Term Objectives	Performance	Unit Results
Integrated Programs	Short-Term Objectives	Individual Results
Financial Projections	Action Plans	Corrective Action
Executive Summary	Budgets	Reward System

This information has been derived from The Executive Guide to Strategic Planning, by Patrick Below, George L. Morrisey, and Betty L. Acomb. Jossey-Bass, San Francisco, 1987.

Figure 1.1

Centralized executive level management of these activities allows rapid and accurate communications between the elements of the strategic planning process shown in Figure 1.1. For example, actions on elements of a strategic plan defining long term projections for adding facilities that are translated into operational plans are reported directly to a chief facilities officer. By regularly reviewing progress on a project with departmental staff, the chief facilities officer is prepared to report progress and results to executive level management on a prompt and fully informed basis.

The Organizational Structure

The facilities management organizational structure is developed by applying general management principles to the unique planning and operational characteristics of buildings, grounds, utilities, and equipment. An operating structure evolves from answering the questions: What? Why? Where? When? and How? The steps followed in developing the organizational structure from an organization's mission to the operating plan are described in the following paragraphs and illustrated in Figure 1.2.

Mission
The basic concept of the organization is defined by the *mission statement*. The primary function of the mission statement is to answer the *what* questions. What business should the organization be in? What is the basic nature and concept of the organization?

Goals and Objectives
Goals and objectives identify the strategic results which would carry out the organization's mission. They are broadly defined and indicate what the organization wishes to have or become in the areas of function, service, productivity, diversification, or growth.

Organizational Characteristics
Organizational characteristics comprise the database used to develop the organizational plan. It includes an analysis of the internal and external factors that are likely to have the greatest impact on the future of the organization. This leads to identifying and prioritizing critical issues that need to be addressed in the plan. For example, an organization with strong involvement in information transfer might combine voice and data communications into a single department to provide these services. This structure would permit close coordination between policy-making and operations.

Practices and Procedures
The when and who of an organization is spelled out in practices and procedures. These procedures translate goals and objectives for an organization into specific results. Accountability is specifically assigned to ensure that results are accomplished. The relationships between physical, fiscal, and human resource operating units and between the facilities departments are outlined.

Resources

The budget plan and operating resources for the facilities management organization are part of the organization's overall fiscal management system. Allocations must adequately meet administrative planning, operations, and capital asset management needs (including plant renewal and additions).

Organization

The effective facilities management organizational structure develops from a clear definition of the basic functions assigned to the unit. Activities may routinely shift from guidance on strategy and policy-making to specific tasks involving facilities design and construction, operations and maintenance, and support services.

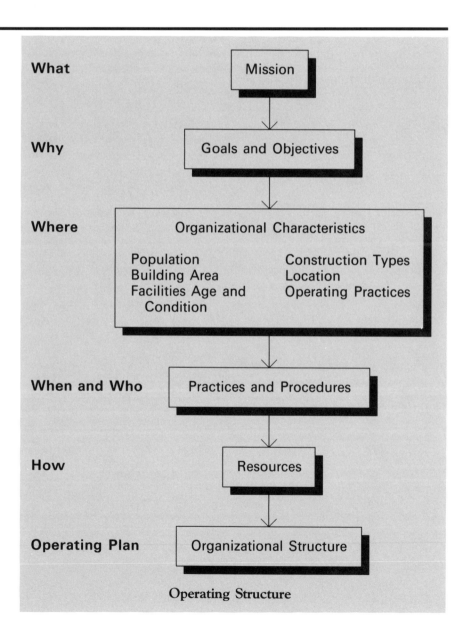

Figure 1.2

The basic functions of a facilities management organizational structure include the following:

- Property management
- Strategic facilities planning
- Capital budgeting
- New construction and renovations
- Space planning and management
- Architectural and engineering services
- Audit and analysis of facilities and management
- Operations and maintenance
- Administrative services

These functional activities can be organized under four major management control units—property management, facilities planning, facilities operations and maintenance, and facilities support services. These areas are illustrated in Figure 1.3.

Management control and these four control functions accomplish the daily activities of managing property, planning to acquire or utilize existing facilities (buildings, grounds, utilities, and equipment), and operating and maintaining physical resources. These components are in constant interaction and, in turn, interact with other management responsibilities to influence short- and long-term policy decisions.

One feature of this particular organizational structure is that the individualized flows of information and operational responsibilities can be accommodated. Tasks or departments for each component can be grouped into configurations tailored to an organization's specific characteristics. For example, the large organization with dispersed locations may have centralized units controlling activities, with only operations, maintenance, and support services fully staffed on a local basis.

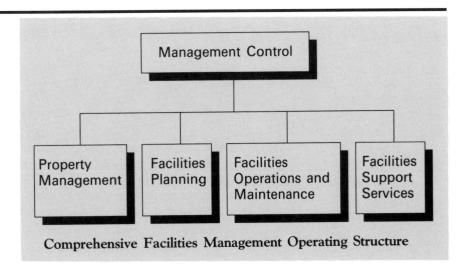

Comprehensive Facilities Management Operating Structure

Figure 1.3

As with all organizational charts, several factors shape the assignment of responsibilities. Traditions and size of an organization dictate the levels and distribution of responsibilities. Location and size of facilities—urban, suburban, or rural, a single, high rise, campus-like setting, or regionally dispersed—affects the number of operating departments and staff. A company's traditional arrangement of function and use of consultants or contractors also influences the new facilities operating structure.

The fundamental principle to remember in setting up an operating structure is that the purpose and functions of the business dictate the organizational arrangement of the facilities management components. For example, a single facility with a limited purpose requires a "tight" organization that can be highly responsive to performance because of visibility and supporting productivity. An organization with several locations and varied functions, such as a utility, requires a centralized management group and methods for dispatching service and specialized service units. Such an organization, in a stable situation, would probably have one consolidated planning and operations group. Conversely, a firm in a period of expansion would require separate planning and operations branches to handle projects and service operations needs for technical advice. Too many layers and components hamper communications, yet too small a staff, dispersed, or uncoordinated departments fail to bring an appropriate flow of information to policy levels or line managers.

Management Control

Direction for the four operating components is provided by the facilities manager, who has the authority and responsibility to direct overall organization. This is the position charged with the diverse roles of acting as a staff advisor to senior management on all facilities matters and supervising the daily activities of the operating units managed by department heads.

The size and specific characteristics of an organization will dictate staffing and resources available to management control. A small facilities management group may operate with an administrative assistant supporting the facilities manager. In this role, the assistant provides direct supervision over a small maintenance department with central personnel, fiscal, and data support. The larger the organization, the more complex a management control unit becomes, with many subdepartments.

The Facilities Manager

The facilities manager should have an academic degree and sufficient practical experience in a professional discipline—either business, architecture, or engineering. The specific degree is not as important as the rigorous educational training and professional practice for the logical organization of facts, seeking alternative solutions, and reaching conclusions on problems of allocating resources. Leadership skills are another important trait of the facilities manager because he must play the multiple roles of decision maker, supervisor, and organizer.

In the course of a day, the facilities manager may move from the boardroom making a presentation on budgets to the bottom of a water-filled pit to look at a water line break. Communicating with corporate management and tradespeople alike, orally or in writing, are other routine tasks of the facilities manager.

The facilities manager is a new type of professional because of the wide scope of responsibilities and skills it takes to do the job. Experience as a supervisor is essential, because assignments must be delegated. Choices of where to focus time and interest must be selective. The ability to anticipate problems and gather the right people to resolve an issue often makes the difference between success and failure in facilities management.

The facilities manager's job may be created because senior management faces difficult decisions about physical resources (and the responsibilities governing the physical resources of a facility are scattered in different departments). The solution is to pull them together under a single manager. Facilities management positions have been created with centralized management responsibilities in private corporations, public agencies, and nonprofit organizations. Manufacturers and banks with dispersed locations; federal, state, and local government; utility companies; colleges and universities; and medical complexes all require comprehensive managers to oversee the physical resources of these diverse facilities.

Property Management Branch

The property management department is the center for making daily decisions on buying, selling, leasing, or building property. Initiative, aggressive action, and confidentiality are essential in these activities. Other tasks include governmental relations involved with environmental land use controls, regulatory requirements, and other local jurisdictional procedures.

There is a close working relationship between strategic planning as developed by senior management and implementation by operating departments to satisfy space needs and fiscal requirements. This suggested operating structure enables facilities staff to carry out management's policy and manage properties in close coordination with planning and operations departments. The chief financial officer (head of management control) can be closely involved in property management decisions.

Facilities Planning Branch

Support on master planning, feasibility studies, design, and construction are provided by a facilities planning branch. A facilities planning department can act as staff to senior management, advising in strategic planning decisions on capital assets by evaluating alternatives and providing recommendations. An example of the advisory role is in coordinating a master plan for new electrical service in combination with consultants.

The size of this department is dictated by the total amount of land and building area of an organization, types of facilities, number of locations, and degree of organizational change.

Facilities Operations and Maintenance Branch

The operations and maintenance functions overlap. For this reason, these activities are usually combined under one entity. Operations refers to the daily functioning of facilities, such as central utilities, and building mechanical and electrical systems. Maintenance ensures that an organization's facilities are kept in continued use in a cost-effective manner. Typical objectives of the operations and maintenance branch are listed below.

- Reduce facility deterioration
- Minimize equipment and structural failures
- Provide a safe, secure, and healthy working environment
- Lower operating and maintenance costs
- Organize an efficient and effective organizational structure that plans, schedules, and measures work activity

Facilities Support Services Branch

This department is a collection of activities that provide support services to overall facilities management. Support services, along with fiscal and data management, may be grouped centrally or decentralized within a facilities management unit. Even when these activities are physically located elsewhere in an organization, they should be managed by one facilities branch. Whatever the choice in organizational structure, the fiscal and data management departments should operate closely with the administrative center of the facilities management organization for consistency of procedures and control.

Summary of Responsibilities

A summary of the operating responsibilities of the five components of facilities management is shown in Figure 1.4. The organization is given overall direction by a facilities manager, or chief facilities officer, reporting directly to corporate management. The facilities manager may also be in charge of the management control unit. Each of the operating components is headed by a manager with technical and management capabilities appropriate to the unit's responsibilities. Each branch under management control is explained in more detail in the next four chapters.

Earlier, the question was posed: Why the need for facilities management? Inefficient practices in managing facilities are luxuries no longer to be tolerated. A coordinated approach to managing an organization's assets has become necessary to properly integrate fiscal, human, and physical resources. Success in facilities management is not achieved by merely engaging in property management, planning, operating, or maintaining facilities, but in managing, under one entity, an organization's capital assets.

Summary of Operating Responsibilities

Management Control
  External Relations
  Organizational Planning
  Resource Allocation
  Functional Coordination and Relationships
  Monitoring Performance
  Audit and Analysis
  Administrative Support

Property Management
  Strategic Property Management
  Real Estate Acquisition, Disposal, and Control
  Lease Management
  Governmental Relations—Land Use, Regulatory
  Financial and Data Management

Facilities Planning
  Strategic Facilities Planning
  Building Design and Construction
  Space Planning: Utilization, Allocation, and Construction
  Interior Design
  Energy Management Planning
  Telecommunications Network Coordination
  Cost Controls and Data Management

Facilities Operations and Maintenance
  Maintenance Management
  Utility Operations
  Facility Maintenance
  Major Maintenance and Renovation
  Grounds Maintenance
  Custodial Services
  Life Safety Systems
  Energy Management Operations
  Material Control
  Transportation and Vehicle Maintenance
  General Services
  Cost Controls and Data Management

Facilities Support Services
  Security
  Telecommunications
  Transportation and Parking
  Mail Services

Figure 1.4

Chapter Two

MANAGEMENT CONTROL

To be most effective, a facilities management program should have a strong management control branch that is clearly separated from the functional divisions of an organization. Management control oversees all other facilities management functions and reports directly to senior managers. Basic responsibilities include planning, resource allocation, monitoring performance, and evaluating results for the various departments and their staff. The characteristics and functions of management control are addressed in this chapter.

Organizational Structure

The organizational structure of management control depends on the size and specific characteristics of an organization. Two basic principles guide the design of the organizational structure. The **staff** or **advisory** function involves reporting to and conferring with senior management and monitoring external relations. These tasks are primarily the responsibility of the facilities manager alone. The **operating** function includes the supervision of the departments or units reporting directly to the facilities manager.

The shape of the organization depends on whether certain activities are included in the facilities management organization or are provided elsewhere. For example, budgeting and accounting, human resources, purchasing, training, safety, or risk management functions may be part of facilities management, or they may be located in other departments of the company. Illustrations of various company organizations are shown in Figure 2.1.

The Facilities Administrator

The facilities administrator is the "chief facilities officer" or facilities manager of an organization. All facilities functions report to this officer to coordinate capital assets. In addition, this position is the principal external representative of the facilities management branch. The facilities administrator should provide broad general policy guidance, and coordinate the work of the individual facilities departments.

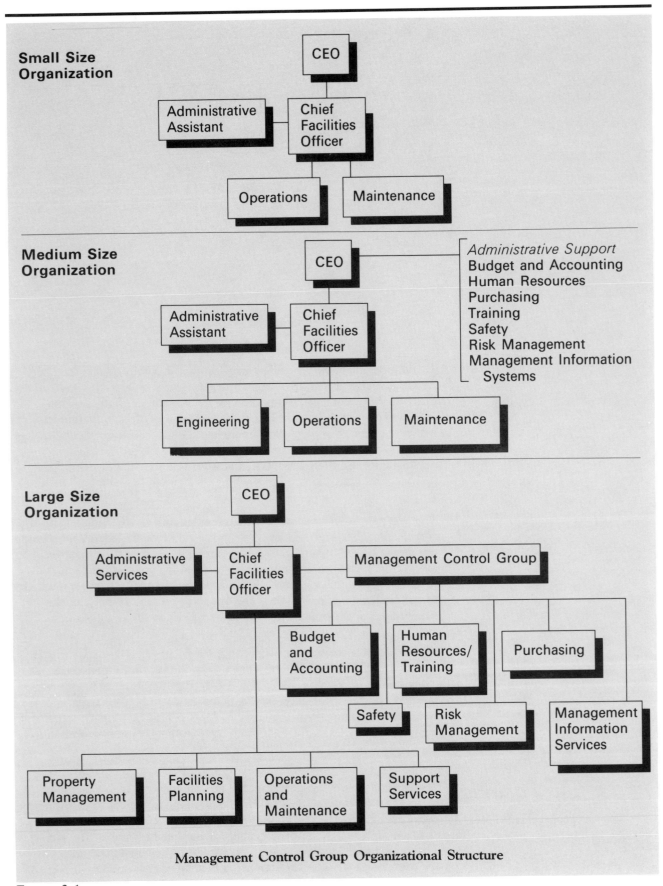

Small Size Organization

CEO

Administrative Assistant — Chief Facilities Officer

Operations   Maintenance

Medium Size Organization

CEO

Administrative Assistant — Chief Facilities Officer

Administrative Support
Budget and Accounting
Human Resources
Purchasing
Training
Safety
Risk Management
Management Information
 Systems

Engineering   Operations   Maintenance

Large Size Organization

CEO

Administrative Services — Chief Facilities Officer — Management Control Group

Budget and Accounting   Human Resources/Training   Purchasing

Safety   Risk Management   Management Information Services

Property Management   Facilities Planning   Operations and Maintenance   Support Services

Management Control Group Organizational Structure

Figure 2.1

16

Placement of the facilities administrator on the organizational chart and exact title may vary. As an organization grows in size, support functions are added to keep up with central organizational activities. A middle layer of management, directly below and reporting to the facilities administrator, may assist in directing reporting departments. The facilities administrator should, preferably, report to a chief administrator who is responsible for overseeing all financial, human resource, and administrative support such as a vice president for finance or administration. It is important to place facilities management on the policy-making level of the organization. Managing such relationships with other major officers of the organization requires special skills for negotiating, in addition to management and technical skills.

Qualifications for the facilities administrator range from prior experience in facilities management and a practical technical background, to professional degrees in architecture or engineering and additional education in business management. Regardless of the facilities administrator's educational qualifications, the most important requirement is broad applicable experience in management in the facilities area. A sample job description of a facilities administrator is shown in Figure 2.2.

Functions of Management Control

The basic functions of the management control branch are managing:
- external relations,
- organizational planning,
- resource planning,
- functional coordination and relationships,
- monitoring performance,
- audit and analysis, and
- administrative support.

These functions are detailed in Figure 2.3 and described in the following paragraphs.

External Relations

Communicating with the public on facilities-related matters is the responsibility of the facilities administrator. External relations include representing the organization with various constituencies; local, state, and federal government; the press and electronic media; and impacted neighboring residents and other property owners. The facilities administrator may also represent the organization on land use, environmental, and property matters.

Traditional responsibilities of external relations have been drastically altered by government regulations and environmental issues. For example, expansion of facilities requiring environmental impact statements will require extensive discussions with the public and the media. Thus, the facilities administrator must be able to supervise preparation of written and graphic presentations, and possess strong interpersonal and communications skills, to manage public interest in the community's economic development.

The facilities administrator informs the public on matters such as growth or contraction, which are generally of intense interest to the local community. Swift, appropriate management of environmental crises and issues is an important practice to maintain credibility and produce relatively favorable responses to unexpected and sometimes catastrophic events. Although support may come from public relations or communications departments of an organization, the facilities administrator is the source and often the public figure presenting such information.

Facilities Administrator—Job Description

The (Corporation) is seeking applications from qualified candidates for the position of Vice President for Facilities Administration. The Vice President for Facilities Administration is a new position created to manage all organizational facilities, and reports directly to the chief executive officer. Responsibilities include: developing strategic facilities planning in an advisory capacity to the corporate planning committee; representing the corporation in external relations and internal coordination between other corporate divisions on facilities related matters; preparing and maintaining the master plan and a capital budget plan for leased and owned facilities; supervising real estate activities on buying, leasing, or selling property; directing design and construction for renovations and capital additions; coordinating and directing operations and maintenance for all corporate buildings, grounds, utilities, and capital equipment; and managing the human and financial resources of the Office of Facilities Administration in a cost-effective and efficient manner.

The Office of Facilities Administration includes the following divisions headed by directors:
1. Management Control—Administrative support (components of human resources, accounting and budgeting, purchasing, and training)
2. Property Management
3. Design and Construction
4. Operations and Maintenance
5. Facilities Support Services: Transportation and Parking, Security, Telecommunications, Mail Services, etc.

Qualifications and Experience
1. B.S. degree in architecture, engineering, or a related discipline.
2. At least ten years experience as a manager in facilities administration.
3. Strong management background with proven ability in public presentations, interacting with all staff and management levels, providing leadership, and effecting change in developing a new approach to facilities administration.
4. Strong interpersonal and communications skills.

Figure 2.2

An external relations program should incorporate the following practices.

- Routinely prepare public information releases introducing and explaining capital projects and status reports.
- Develop procedures for community outreach programs and crises management on facilities matters.
- Prepare presentations for: local, state, and federal governments; community groups; and service organizations.
- Provide a readily accessible and up-to-date database and graphic materials on facilities activities.
- Produce attractive and informative annual reports.
- Procure adequate support for legal advice.

Organizational Planning

The objective of planning is to ensure that the activities of facilities administration are carried out effectively and efficiently.

Functions of Management Control

External Relations

    Local, State, and Federal Governments
    Community Relations
    External Relations Programs

Organizational Planning

    Goals and Objectives
    Policies and Procedures

Resource Allocation

    Budgeting
    Work Load Planning
    Priority Selection

Functional Coordination and Relationships Within an Organization

Monitoring Performance

    Performance Reviews
    Performance Standards
    Quality of Performance

Audit and Analysis

    Management Audit
    Facilities Audit

Administrative Support

    Budget and Accounting
    Human Resources
    Purchasing
    Training
    Safety
    Risk Management
    Management Information Systems

Figure 2.3

The management control group sets goals and objectives for the organization. Policies and procedures translate overall goals and objectives into guidelines for facilities management. How effectively the overall aims of the organization are met depends on how thoroughly the implementation of each goal and objective is planned.

The management control group is responsible for the organizational planning tasks listed below.

- Identify and communicate departmental goals and objectives.
- Prepare, implement, and update operating policies as required by goals and objectives.
- Prepare procedures needed to support policy implementation.
- Define responsibilities of department directors and delegate authority.
- Maintain a functional organizational structure as defined by goals and objectives.

Organizational planning for goals, objectives, policies, and procedures can operate at various levels. A "low" level is characterized by information developed orally and delegated by specific written assignment. "Medium" level includes written general and specific guidelines. Written guidelines may take the form of a Policies and Procedures Manual. A "high" level of organizational planning incorporates formal and published information. A sample Policies and Procedures Manual outline for an operations and maintenance department is shown in Figure 2.4.

Resource Allocation

The management control group supervises the resource allocation process for annual operations and capital expenditures. Resource allocation is a continuous process encompassing all phases of operations and personnel within the organization. The supervisory tasks in the resource allocation process include the selection of priorities and work load planning. The priorities can be forming a team to respond to a management request for a feasibility study, or overseeing a hazardous material problem. Work load planning monitors the adequacy of staffing to achieve goals and objectives of each operating department.

Allocation of facilities administration resources is guided by annual and long term goals and objectives in a three-part process: 1) preparation of budgets; 2) implementation of budgets; and 3) budget management and control.

Preparation of budgets proceeds from an evaluation of past budgets, projected expenses, and income. One of the most important measures in evaluating the performance of facilities administration is the ability to operate within its budget. The chief facilities officer should carefully plan anticipated costs to ensure that funds are available to meet expenses.

Implementation of budgets is the performance of work in conformance with allocated resources. This responsibility is delegated to the directors of operating departments by the chief facilities officer. This is more than accounting for expenses. It means **managing** to redistribute and balance staff among planning, operations, maintenance, renovations, and capital projects. Contract services may be required and funds reallocated from budgeted staff, material, and equipment purchases.

Budget management and control is based on accounting information. Costs are reported on employee payroll, material and equipment purchases, and contract services. Reports based on the accounting information provide feedback to management control to analyze the progress of budget implementation. Comparison of planned to actual expenses and income, and analyses of trends permit adjustments to maintain a balanced budget or request additional funding for unanticipated expenditures. If financial difficulties arise, the chief facilities officer is prepared with information to make sound decisions on budget reductions.

**Policies and Procedures Manual Outline for an
Operations and Maintenance Department**

General
Objectives and Goals
Relations to other Operating Departments

Organization and Staffing
Organizational Structure
Job Descriptions

Maintenance System Overview
Budgeting
Initiating Work
Planning
Scheduling
Executing
Reporting

Purchasing and Material Control
Purchasing Procedures
Competitive Bidding
Supervision and Contract Administration
Payment Procedures
Material Inventories
Equipment Records

Cost Accounting
Accounting Records
Payroll Data
Accounting Methods

Performance Evaluation
Reports
Performance Standards
Analyses and Feedback

Appendices

Figure 2.4

Budgets consist of expenses related to immediate objectives (such as routine maintenance) and long range objectives (such as capital construction projects). The budget period for operations may be **annual** or **biannual**, depending upon the organization's traditional practices. Capital budgets can extend for the duration of a strategic planning period, based on capitalization procedures, or for the duration of individual capital projects.

Four main cost elements that must be considered in the resource allocation process are personnel, materials, equipment, and contracted services.

Personnel: Each department should account for all personnel it employs. A job description should exist for each employee. Numbers of personnel in any one category should be determined on the basis of the work that must be performed by that department during a given period of time. Historical data, work standards, and efficiency studies can be used to support the level of personnel required.

Material: All material purchases anticipated for the coming year should be included in this category. Generally, expendable materials are monitored to control inventory at reasonable levels.

Equipment: Specific involvement in this category depends upon the definitions set by the organization's budget officer for expendable materials and capitalized equipment. Once these categories have been established, the management control group should be consistent in applying the definitions.

Contract Services: Staffing the facilities administration functions is achieved by balancing a budget base of personnel, materials, and work performed by outside contractors.

Consultants can vary from elevator maintenance and cleaning to technical services for architecture and engineering. Contract services may be performed on an annual basis for specific projects.

Whenever possible, competition should be sought for contracted services. Purchasing departments and those charged with doing business with outside firms have found it easier to have the work done by one reliable firm. However, problems may arise if a contractor assumes that no other company will compete for the job and consequently overprices the work.

Functional Coordination and Relationships

Facilities management interacts with other departments of an organization in providing and receiving support services. Such interactions must be standardized. Routine maintenance work and special work requests must have standard methods for service delivery. These methods include published procedures, forms, and staff assignments. The management control group sets the service standards and monitors adherence to organizational procedures for accounting, purchasing, training, and database management. Coordination of the management control branch's functional relationships with other departments is established by performing the following tasks.

- Clearly define facilities administration operating department responsibilities and practices that are differentiated from other departments of the organization.

- Maintain effective liaison and influence decisions on programs, planning processes, and operations in financial, human resources, and other functional units of the organization.
- Inform other departments of special projects potentially interrupting operations.
- Ensure that physical locations and operating relationships among central administrative support promote efficiency, effectiveness, and economy in these operations.
- Delineate and inform members of the organization of the role, actions, and responsibilities of facilities administration personnel in emergency situations, ranging from labor disputes to natural disasters.
- Define procedures for requests for services and changes in spaces use.
- Resolve any undefined areas of responsibility for operations and maintenance of buildings, grounds, and equipment.

Monitoring Performance

Monitoring performance of a service unit such as facilities administration is usually thought of as cost control. However, this is too limiting a definition of performance. Simply because a department has met its budgets does not necessarily mean that it has performed successfully.

Management should consider the following questions to monitor performance:

1. How efficiently and effectively have the departments used their available resources to meet organizational and departmental goals and objectives?
2. Have levels of service met performance standards?
3. Has the performance of individuals been evaluated?
4. Have customers been surveyed for opinions on performance quality?

These questions are answered by evaluating: individual staff members through **performance reviews**; productivity of the departments by **performance standards**; and service performance by measuring **quality of performance**.

Performance Reviews: Performance reviews are standard instruments that may already exist in the organization. If they do not, they should be adopted for regular annual use. The form shown in Figure 2.5 is part of an evaluation process designed to be administered by supervisory personnel for all staff in the organization.

The performance review process should start with an orientation for supervisors to understand the purpose and content of the evaluation. It should be stressed that the process provides a record of the employee's demonstrated, not anticipated, performance. Requirements of the specific position should be considered and a job description referred to, if necessary. Strengths and weaknesses, and suggestions for improvements, are valuable parts of the process. After completing the form, an interview should be held with the employee to review the evaluation. A signed copy of the form is forwarded to the responsible department as part of the employee's permanent record.

STAFF PERFORMANCE EVALUTION

Employee's Name _____ Evaluation Date _____
Department _____ Job Title _____
Supervisor _____

Instructions: The Performance Evaluation Form is to be prepared by the supervisor before interviewing the employee. At the end of the conference, a copy is provided to the employee to repond with comments. A signed copy is returned to the supervisor and forwarded to the department head.

Rating Scale: 1 = Performance meets job requirements
                     2 = Performance is below acceptable levels
                     3 = Does not apply

PERFORMANCE

(Circle One)

1. **Job Knowledge:** understanding of job duties   1   2   3
   and responsibilites and relationships to the
   other department positions.
   Comments:_____
   _____

2. **Accomplishments:** amount of work produced in   1   2   3
   relation to expectations, goals, and objectives.
   Comments:_____
   _____

3. **Quality:** thoroughness of work; following   1   2   3
   instructions, rules, policies, and regulations;
   neatness; accuracy.
   Comments_____
   _____

4. **Technical Skills:** ability to use appropriate   1   2   3
   methods, equipment, and materials to accomplish work.
   Comments_____
   _____

5. **Analytical Skills:** judgement; problem-solving,   1   2   3
   decision-making.
   Comments:_____
   _____

Figure 2.5

6. **Resource Management:** direction, training, and   1   2   3
   motivation of staff.
   Comments:_____

   _____

   Use of funds, equipment.
   Comments:_____

   _____

7. **Communications:** oral presentations, interviews,   1   2   3
   memos, letters, reports.
   Comments:_____

   _____

8. **Affirmative Action:** awareness and implementation   1   2   3
   of Affirmative Action policies and responsibilities.
   Comments:_____

   _____

9. **Relations with other members of the organization**   1   2   3
   and external contacts: service orientation,
   professionalism, and thoroughness.
   Comments:_____

   _____

FACTORS INFLUENCING PERFORMANCE

1. **Attitude:** sensitivity to goals and needs of the   1   2   3
   department and organization; cooperation with
   others; courtesy, enthusiasm; willingness to work
   with integrity.
   Comments:_____

   _____

2. **Reliability:** fulfilling duties and responsibilties;   1   2   3
   meeting of schedules, deadlines; punctuality, attend-
   ance, and dependability.
   Comments:_____

   _____

3. **Resourcefulness:** initiative, creativity and follow-   1   2   3
   through in working job objectives.
   Comments:_____

   _____

4. **Interpersonal Skills:** ability to achieve effective   1   2   3
   working relationships.
   Comments:_____

   _____

Figure 2.5 (continued)

5. **Self-improvement:** job-related development of
   skills; completion of courses, seminars, work-
   shops, and staff development programs; reading
   of appropriate journals, periodicals, and books.
   Comments: _____

   _____

Supervisor's Comments:

_____

_____

_____

_____   _____

Supervisor's Signature   Date

Employee's Comments:

_____

_____

_____

_____   _____

Employee's Signature   Date

_____   _____

Department Head   Date

Figure 2.5 (continued)

Performance Standards: Performance standards are developed by the management control group to measure productivity of employees. Various reports should be designed for planning and scheduling work, to monitor work performance, and to summarize reports for management review. Standards are applicable primarily for service areas in operations and maintenance. *Means Facilities Maintenance Standards* by Gregory Magee (R.S. Means Company, Inc., 1988) provides guidelines for developing standard work performance measures.

Quality of Performance: Quality of performance is a recent innovation in American corporate life. Its purpose is to evaluate the quality of a product or service provided to a customer in order to improve performance and raise customer satisfaction. The key concepts are **customer** and **provider**. Service organizations tend to forget that they are in business to satisfy customers. Setting goals and methods of evaluation are necessary to correct poor quality standards.

Quality of performance should differ from quantitative analysis of productivity because customer satisfaction is more difficult to measure (for service organizations). Basic questions to be examined are:

- What is the quality of performance in the delivery of service?
- Is the customer accurately defining the request for service?
- Is the provider confirming the request to ensure timely and appropriate delivery of service?

The simplest device to begin the process of improving performance quality is a well-prepared, **organizational survey** of opinions of service. Risky as it sounds, a survey asking customers' opinions uncovers areas of dissatisfaction that can initiate revisions in methods of managing and delivering services. A performance quality survey form for a Facilities Planning Office is illustrated in Figure 2.6.

All service departments should conduct performance quality surveys. Schedules of evaluations for departments should be prepared by the management control group, allowing adequate time for evaluation and review with the surveyed department heads and supervisory personnel. Recommendations for improvements and an implementation program is the responsibility of the surveyed department. Follow-up reviews provide management with benchmarks for measuring progress on changes in organizational structure, procedures, and supervision.

Audit and Analysis

The management control group supervises and analyzes results for a Management Audit and a Facilities Audit. These are not financial audits, but review the performance of management and the conditions of facilities. The Facilities Audit is described in Chapters 8 through 11. The Management Audit is described below.

Management Audit: The purpose of a Management Audit is to ensure that management is carrying out its mission, meeting its goals and objectives, following procedures, and managing resources effectively and efficiently. The Management Audit process is shown in Figure 2.7.

PERFORMANCE QUALITY SURVEY - FACILITIES PLANNING OFFICE

Clients who in the past have had work done by the Office of
Facilities Planning

Department _____   Date_____
Project _____   Name _____

1. What was the nature of the work and services performed by or
   requested of the Facilities Planning Office?
   _____ Upgrading of existing space, equipment, systems, or
         furniture
   _____ Modification of space to accommodate a change in your
         departments' functions, size, or organizational
         relationship
   _____ Construction of and relocation to a new building
   _____ Renovation of and relocation to an existing building
   _____ Assistance with development of the scope of work for a
         proposed project
   _____ Preparation of cost estimate or feasiblity study
   _____ Preparation of design studies, construction drawings,
         and specifications
   _____ Other (Specify)_____

2. Did you deal directly with the Facilities Planning Office or
   through an intermediary?
   _____ Yes _____ No
   If no, who was the intermediary department?_____

3. Did you find the Facilities Office Personnel to be:

	Yes	No
Courteous?	_____	_____
Conscientious?	_____	_____
Knowledgable of their work?	_____	_____
Willing to respond to requests?	_____	_____

4. What was the funding source for the above referenced project?

   _____

5. Prior to commencing the design work, was there a formal
   understanding between the requesting unit and Facilities
   Planning describing the scope of the project?
   _____ Yes _____ No

   If yes, by whom was it prepared?

   _____

Figure 2.6

6. During development of the design and details, did you participate in periodic reviews of the drawings and specifications?
   _____ Yes _____ No

   If yes, did you understand the final design?
   _____ Yes _____ No, (Explain)_____

7. Cost Estimates
   a. Did you receive estimates of the costs involved?
      Prior to design?   _____ Yes _____ No
      During design?   _____ Yes _____ No
      Prior to construction start?   _____ Yes _____ No

   b. Did you make changes to job scope after estimates were received?
                                         _____ Yes _____ No

   c. If yes, was it explained to you that changes might affect the cost?
                                         _____ Yes _____ No

8. How close was the estimate to the final cost?
   _____ Lower than the estimate _____%
   _____ Equal to the estimate _____%
   _____ Higher than the estimate _____%

9. Were the requirements, as defined in writing, met by the design?
                                         _____ Yes _____ No
   (Explain) _____

10. Who performed the construction work?
    _____ In-house staff
    _____ Outside contractor
    _____ Combination of the two

11. Were you satisfied with the work?
    _____ Yes _____ No, (Explain) _____

12. Considering the work requirements, both original and revised, are you satified that the cost was reasonable?
    _____ Yes _____ No, (Explain) _____

Figure 2.6 (*continued*)

13. Were both the planning and execution of the work carried out in a timely manner?

_____ Yes _____ No, (Explain) _____

14. Have you ever had a need for the services of the Facilities Planning Office that, for whatever reason, could not be addressed?

_____ Yes _____ No, (Explain) _____

15. Please add any other comments or suggestions.

_____
_____
_____
_____
_____
_____
_____
_____
_____

Thank You!

Return to: _____
           _____
           _____

Figure 2.6 (continued)

Preliminary suggestions for conducting the Management Audit are:

- The audit should assess the right things. It must appraise performance in light of sound management principles. Objectives and scope must be clearly defined to ensure a constructive appraisal of an operation's effectiveness.
- The audit should include the participation of the department being reviewed.
- The audit should be objective and constructive. Every effort should be made to ensure that all review participants maintain independent, constructive perspectives.
- The evaluation should be acceptable. Any management technique or program that people do not understand and accept is likely to be ineffective.

Procedure: The basic phases, steps and functional assignments in the management audit process are described below. There can be many variations on the central framework, depending upon an organization's size, management style and organizational structure. At a smaller organization some of the steps could be quite informal. Formal, coordinated steps might be necessary at a larger institution.

Phase I—Establish Priorities and Schedule Reviews:

1. Prepare a draft review schedule and nominate activities to be reviewed; suggest priorities and review time frames.
2. Set priorities among areas to be reviewed; issue schedule.

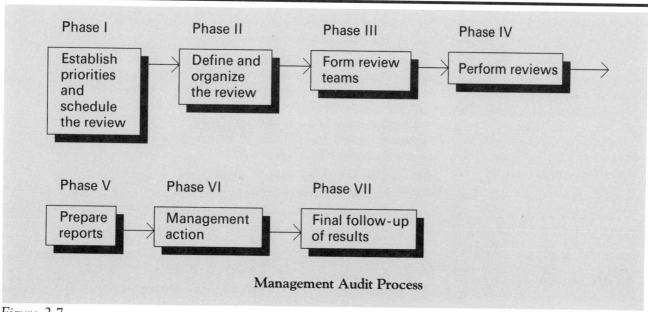

Management Audit Process

Figure 2.7

Phase II—Define and Organize the Review:
1. Review functional areas and procedures pertinent to the functional area; identify potential review team members.
2. Establish coordination with department manager(s); discuss purpose of review, potential review team members, participation, and timing.
3. Prepare and send questionnaires to department manager(s).
4. Assemble data about the review area.
5. Prepare preliminary statement of the scope of the review:
    a. Identify the limits of the project.
    b. Prepare a statement of objectives.
    c. Establish a work plan:
        1) Review possible methods of analysis and data collection.
        2) Identify criteria to be used in evaluating unit performance.
        3) Determine necessary coordinating procedures.
        4) Identify review tasks.
        5) Estimate resources needed to conduct the work.
        6) Estimate time requirements.

A high grade performance by the evaluation coordinator and staff in the second phase enables the review team to carry out its assignment economically, efficiently, and effectively. Three things must happen. First, the coordinator discusses the proposed review with the department manager of the selected unit. Next, the staff begins assembling pertinent data and information which will be turned over to the review team. Finally, a definition of the parameters of the review, and an indication of some of the processes to be examined, are proposed in a statement of the scope of the review.

Phase III—Form the Review Team:
1. Select members for the review team and arrange with department heads for members' participation.
2. Familiarize the review team with functional areas and style of work.
3. Confirm and adopt statement of scope of review.
4. Confirm work plan with department manager(s).
5. Discuss methods and procedures with the review team.
6. Prepare detailed task plans using functional area outline and orientation material previously assembled by staff.
7. Assign specific tasks to team members.

The coordinator should take the lead in selecting the review team members, and securing from their respective department directors a temporary release from standing commitments. A key task before any further action is the adoption of a written statement of the scope of the review. This leads to the review team's work plan, time schedule, and assignment of tasks to individual members. The importance of a scope statement cannot be overemphasized.

Phase IV—Perform the Review:
1. Collect data: review policies and procedures, conduct interviews with unit staff, utilize additional questionnaires of opinion polls, review budget documents.
2. Analyze data: organize the data for analysis. Tabulate survey information, summarize, and organize interview data, and then interpret the data.
3. Identify organizational, process, and service problems.

The review team carries out its active work of analyzing problems revealed from the information and data collected. This involves personal observations and interviews both in and around the unit being audited. In review team meetings, impressions should be clarified and synthesized until the team is ready to make recommendations.

Phase V—Prepare the Report:

1. Formulate recommendations of alternative approaches to operations and organizations to assist management in solving identified problems.
2. Determine report format and content.
3. Assign drafting responsibilities; prepare draft of report.
4. Discuss, evaluate, and revise the draft report.
5. Discuss the draft report with department manager(s).
6. Prepare a final report and present it to the steering committee.
7. Review, approve and distribute the final report.

Whether or not the review produces tangible results depends largely on how well Phases V and VI are handled. The review team's central task is to prepare a report for senior management on the audited unit's degree of success in meeting its objectives and on the unit's major strengths and weaknesses. The report also makes recommendations for management action.

Phase VI—Management Action:

1. Submit a plan of action responding to review team recommendations.
2. Assess review team report and action plan from department manager(s); discuss with department manager(s) and supervisor, if necessary.
3. Evaluate and approve recommendations to be carried out by department manager(s).
4. Obtain agreement from department manager(s) and supervisor.

In Phase VI, the organization's determination to effectively manage its resources is tested and demonstrated. The department manager responds to the review team's final report by proposing a plan of action. After assessing the potential effectiveness of the plan (in meeting the report's findings and recommendations), agreement must be obtained on a systematic course of action. The department manager and the supervisor are expected to initiate the necessary changes indicated in the report.

Phase VII—Final Follow-Up of Results:

1. Monitor the implementation process.
2. Submit a progress report on implementation to the steering committee.
3. Critique review activity and results (include evaluation of project methodology, suggestions for changes in procedures, etc.).
4. Submit closing report to steering committee and chief executive officer.

During Phase VII, the evaluation's effectiveness as a long-range tool comes into focus. Achieving the goals towards which the department manager's plan is geared may take anywhere from several months to more than a year. Desired outcomes may not be perceptible until a similar amount of time has elapsed. Throughout the process the department manager reports on the progress of implementing actions and the ultimate achievement of results. The review cycle comes to a close with a brief, final report on the review and a summary of the results achieved.

Implementing the results of a management audit will yield the greatest results to the facilities management organization. The management control group is responsible for this task. An example of an implementation program for a maintenance department is shown in Figure 2.8.

Management Audit Implementation Program

1. **Organize Project Task Force**
   Identify task force members
   Develop overall work plan and schedule

2. **Define Total Work Management System**
   A total work management system can be built on the existing organizational structure but requires definition of basic system concepts for functional areas: budgeting, initiating work, planning, scheduling, execution, control and reporting.

   Evaluate operations for each functional area
   Review maintenance operations in reference to budget goals
   Examine and clarify procedures for initiating and processing work orders
   Define planning of maintenance work orders for types of work
   Improve existing scheduling practices
   Formulate operating procedures for field supervision
   Define reporting and control concepts

3. **Design and Document Maintenance Procedures**
   Design appropriate forms and management reports
   Write detailed procedures required to perform specific assignments
   Provide adequate documentation for training purposes
   Develop monitoring procedures for updating work management system

4. **Train Maintenance Supervisors**
   Review and explain concept of work management system to supervisors
   Explain detailed working procedures to supervisors
   Provide on-the-job training for supervision

5. **Monitor System Implementation**
   Develop performance objectives within guidelines of a detailed implementation program
   Review task force responsibilities and appropriate target dates
   Organize material into a comprehensive maintenance procedures manual
   Coordinate stated performance objectives with contingency plans for fiscal objectives
   Prepare updating procedures for the system

Figure 2.8

Administrative Support

The management control group provides administrative support for the facilities management organization. In the small organization, this can be limited to an administrative assistant and other services provided from other departments. In medium and large size organizations, staff is expanded to complete support units detached from central services.

The functions supporting facilities management are:

- Budget and accounting
- Human resources
- Purchasing
- Training
- Safety
- Risk management
- Management information systems

Organizational configurations for different size organizations are shown in Figure 2.1. The majority of these functions are standard in their responsibilities and procedures. As such, they do not need to be covered in this book. However, training is of special importance to facilities administration and is described in detail in the following paragraphs.

Training: Employee training is an effective management tool when carefully planned and prepared. It should be viewed as an employee development program. The need for training exists at all levels of the facilities management organization—administrators, supervisors, and regular employees. Regardless of the knowledge and experience brought to the job, there are different types of training sessions, with varying purposes. These are:

- orientation or basic training,
- programs that provide further training and additional skills,
- communicating information about the organization,
- improving employee relations, and
- improving productivity.

Training programs may be initiated and coordinated by the human resources department of an organization. In-house personnel or outside trainers may be used. The advantages of using in-house personnel are cost savings, flexibility in scheduling, and training specific to the organization and job. Outside trainers, screened in advance, can provide unavailable expertise, teaching skills, well-prepared materials, and evaluation techniques.

Another alternative is courses provided by professional organizations, commercial sources, or local schools and colleges. An often overlooked source of informal training may be provided by fellow employees. The sharing of information, new skills, and methods should be encouraged by management.

The following criteria for selecting training programs should be used to evaluate suitability or appropriateness.

- **Objectives:** Is the program designed to bring worthwhile improvements to the organization or individual?
- **Appropriateness:** Are program contents appropriate to the needs of administrators, supervisors, and other personnel?
- **Suitability:** Is the program suitable for the expected level of experience of the participant group?

- **Content:** Is there sufficient depth and comprehensiveness in the training material to fit the needs of the participant group and individuals?
- **Quality of Trainers:** Are the trainers knowledgeable in their field, able to motivate, and communicate?

Summary

The leadership of a facilities management organization rests with the chief facilities officer. A management control group, headed by the chief facilities officer, directs the activities of the facilities organization. Depending on the size and characteristics of the parent organization, the facilities management control group ranges in size from a small administrative support group to a collection of departments. The departments may report directly to the chief facilities officer or be organized as detached components of the parent organization or a combination of both.

The functional responsibilities of the management control group include: external relations; organizational planning; resource allocation; functional coordination and relationships within an organization; monitoring performance; audit and analysis; and administrative support.

Chapter Three

PROPERTY MANAGEMENT

Real property managers in the facilities management organization act in a variety of capacities, depending upon the number and types of properties owned and/or leased and real estate activities. The property manager's job may be as simple as paying mortgages, rent, and utilities, and arranging for cleaning and maintenance. Or, the tasks may include managing a portfolio of properties worth hundreds of millions of dollars in worldwide locations.

The Why's of Property Management

Real property, defined as land, structures, or equipment, is an important organizational asset. Current estimates are that American companies have real estate valued at approximately one trillion dollars, representing 25% of their assets. This total is matched only by the holdings of nonprofit institutions, with real property approximately one-half their assets.

Managing these assets may be traditionally delegated to a business officer or real estate department to pay or collect rents, operate, and manage properties. The value of these physical assets requires a close tie to the organization's resources for facilities management to ensure the highest net return over the useful life of the property.

Organizational Relationships

The property manager may act as a staff person, operating and managing properties at the basic level of activities. Record keeping of property files and costs are typical tasks. Site selection advice to carry out strategic plans may also be required.

Responsibilities expand as the real property holdings increase. In the large organization, property management can become a complex department involved in various levels of strategic, operational, and project planning. In strategic planning, the property manager advises on actions to implement long range goals and objectives. This can include site selection and choosing between alternatives to buy, build, lease, or sell property.

Operational planning addresses detailed implementation of strategic plans or expanding current operational activities of administering a department and managing properties. **Project planning** works on specific assignments outside of the day-to-day responsibilities of property management.

Property Management Department Functions

The functions of a property management department are summarized in Figure 3.1 as advising and managing buy, build, lease, and sell decisions for the organization.

Functions of Property Management

Strategic Property Management
Strategic Planning and Facilities Management
Life Cycle Analysis
Organizational Stage of Maturity

Acquire Real Property
Site Selection
Appraisals
Construct
Lease
Purchase

Dispose Real Property
Appraisals
Reassignment
Space Utilization Review
Sell

Operate Real Property
Maintain
Provide Utilities
Furnish
Renewal and Replacements

Administration
Marketing
Renting
Cost Controls
Data Files
Reports

Government Relations
Land Use
Zoning
Community Impact
Environmental Controls
Building Codes
Other Regulations

Figure 3.1

The Property Manager

The chief administrator for the property management department is the property manager. Actual titles for this position may vary based on the preference of the organization; Director of Real Estate is commonly used. Qualifications, tasks, and operating relationships for the property manager are described in the following paragraphs.

Qualifications

The educational background of the property manager should include training in finance and real estate. The need for certification as a real estate broker depends on the organization's holdings, nature, and amount of activities. Experience and knowledge of budgets and accounting, supervision of rental operations, leasing methods, and legal processes are essential requirements to manage a property management department. Skills and experience in managing staff, communicating effectively, and coordinating technical advice from architects, engineers, accountants, appraisers, legal staff, and other consultants are also required.

Tasks

The functional tasks of the property manager in an organization with a varied mix of owned, leased, and owned-leased properties may include:

- Site selection
- Acquisition
- Sale
- Management of leased properties
- Management of owner-leased properties
- Investment property management
- Data file management, cost controls, and reports

Confidentiality

Sensitivity of real estate transactions, where a whisper of plans can cause land or building prices to soar and introduce speculation, require extreme confidentiality. Although a real estate department or staff may provide information on a transaction under consideration, negotiations and final decisions should remain with senior management. All staff should be aware of the sensitivity of policy decisions and reminded of the need for confidentiality.

External holding companies are often set up as a "blind" to conceal transactions and prevent speculation. An outside real estate company or law firm may be retained to manage the transaction. These are traditionally used techniques to conceal land assembly projects prior to the announcement of plans.

Policies and Procedures

One responsibility of the property manager is to prepare policies and procedures to guide an organization's desired goals for managing real property. These should be in agreement with the organizational lines of authority and responsibility and have the approval of senior management. An outline for a policies and procedures document is shown in Figure 3.2.

Relationships

Relationships and resources for property managers may be available within an organization or require outside supplementary guidance. The following professional skills are included in property management's support at one time or another.

- **Financial:**   Analyses and supervision of debt management
  Tax considerations of assessment and
       valuation
  Accounting
  Cost controls
- **Legal:**   Transactions
  Document preparation
  Litigation
- **Design:**   Building design
  Utility and site engineering
  Interior design
  Cost estimates
- **Plant Operation:**   Analyses of operations and maintenance
  Work standards
  Performance measures

Property Management Policies and Procedures Outline

A. Policies and Definitions
1. Authority
2. Definitions
3. Property Management Office

B. Purchasing Real Estate
1. Planning and Site Evaluation
2. Negotiations
3. Required Documents
4. Execution

C. Disposing of Real Estate
1. Appraisals
2. Disposition Policy
3. Space Utilization Review
4. Title Transfer
5. Disposition of Proceeds

D. Management of Leased or Owned-Leased Properties
1. Execution Authority
2. Leasing Policies and Documents
3. Alterations and Improvements
4. Funding Leases
5. Lease Payments and Collections

E. Reports
1. Reporting Periods and Requirements
   a) Owned
   b) Leased
   c) Owned-Leased
2. Property Data File

Figure 3.2

- **Environmental:** Supervising preparation of environmental impact statements in conformance with environmental regulations
- **Economists:** Advice on site selection
Economic impact analysis
Economic projections

Occasional opportunities arise to develop land or facilities for investment purposes. After goals and objectives are determined, the decision is made to buy, build, lease, or sell a property. At this stage, various development strategies can be explored. Some development strategies are:

- **Corporate Responsibility:** A corporate team for development can be created with the support of key consultants. The team should be carefully selected based on experience with similar projects.
- **Developer Assistance:** A corporate decision is made to use outside developers to guide a project. A corporate project manager is appointed to supervise the project and the process of final decision on recommendations.
- **Developer Responsibility:** The entire development process is turned over to outside developers to use corporate resources and manage a project. A corporate officer has final authority to approve a project.

Regardless of which strategy is used, the process should adhere to established policies and involve appropriate legal and financial advice. The selection of specialized experts and managers is based on experience in similar or related procedures. The scope and costs of services of several experts should be compared to obtain a competitive price.

Strategic Property Management

The key to managing an organization's real property—its land, buildings, and equipment—is recognizing the close connection between overall strategic planning and facilities management in making property-related decisions. Real property is a physical asset and, therefore, should be supervised by the facilities management department of an organization.

The skills and information for analyzing alternate ways of meeting investment goals and space needs are available from the other facilities management departments. Technical skills in evaluating the best use of land, alternative uses of existing buildings, or design concepts for new construction and additions are available in a facilities planning department. This unit may also coordinate interior design, purchase of fixtures, furniture, equipment, and relocations.

The operations and maintenance department may provide cost estimates of required services from historic data or obtain comparable data from other sources. The facilities support services department may provide proposals for levels of services and costs for their responsibilities.

The total facilities management department can be used by property management to provide guidance on space needs. For example, the decision to expand an existing operation requires investigations for alternative choices of actions: additions and new construction; purchase of land and new construction; selling existing property; or leasing land and space. The technical resources are available in either the facilities management department of an organization or in combination with consultants coordinated by these departments.

The property management department advises policy-makers in developing strategic property management decisions. Activities involved in strategic property management include:

- Master planning
- Feasibility studies of land use or building alternatives
- Inspections of existing structures
- Preliminary architectural and engineering designs and cost estimates
- Analyses of regulations for land use, zoning, environmental, and building codes
- Operations and maintenance costs
- Support services costs: telecommunications, special transportation needs, parking, and security

Life Cycle Analysis

A useful technique for assessing alternatives in strategic property management is application of life cycle analysis principles. Decisions to buy, build, lease, or sell deal with costs over time. Life cycle analysis deals with both present and future costs and attempts to relate the two as a basis for making decisions. A definition of life cycle cost analysis from the *Life Cycle Cost Analysis: A Guide for Architects*, American Institute of Architects, Washington, D.C., 1977 is:

> "Any technique which allows assessment of a given solution or choice among alternative solutions on the basis of considering all relevant economic consequences over time."

The basic elements in a life cycle cost analysis are **today dollars**, **tomorrow dollars**, and **discount rates**. Basic procedures of an analysis use the following steps. (The reader is also referred to Chapter 5 of *Facilities Maintenance Management*, by Gregory H. Magee, P.E., R.S. Means Company, Inc., 1988, for a thorough discussion of life cycle analysis.)

1. *Establish Objectives of the Analysis*: Is it to assess the consequences of a given decision, such as replacing a roof, or to choose among alternatives on the basis of economic return, such as to build, buy, or lease new space?

2. *Formulate the Alternative to be Analyzed*: Describe the alternatives with criteria appropriate to the analysis subject.

3. *Decide on the Time Period for the Analysis*: A discount rate is elected for a period of years. This may be based on the useful life of a building or the organization's goals for a rate of return.

4. *Identify Cost Factors*: Cost factors are selected to be included in an analysis. Possible factors included in a life cycle analysis are shown in Figure 3.3.

5. *Determine the Life Cycle Cost for a Common Time Period*: Either Total Present Worth or Uniform Annual Cost methods are selected for a discount rate.

6. *Carry out the Analysis*: Outline the format for analysis, perform calculations, and prepare conclusions and recommendations.

7. *Analyze the Results*: Alternative choices can be ranked for meeting objectives.

Cost Factors in the Life Cycle Analysis

1. **Initial Capital Investment**

    Costs associated with initial planning, design, and construction
     - Site acquisition
     - Site surveys and testing
     - Design related fees
     - Moving and relocation
     - Demolition of existing (less salvage)
     - Construction
     - Construction supervision and other owner's costs

2. **Financing Costs**

    Costs associated with financing capital investment
     - One time financing costs
     - Interim construction financing

3. **Operations and Maintenance Costs**

    Costs associated with restoring the facility to its original condition
     - Routine maintenance and cleaning
     - Utilities
     - Taxes (if applicable)
     - Contract services

4. **Repair and Replacement Costs**

    Costs associated with restoring the facility to its original performance
     - Major renovations
     - Major replacements
     - Non-annual maintenance and repairs

5. **Facility Alterations and Improvements Costs**

    Costs associated with planned additions, alterations, major reconfigurations, and other improvements
     - Additions
     - Alterations

6. **Functional Use Costs**

    Costs associated with performing intended functions of the facility
     - Staff salaries and benefits
     - Supplies
     - Taxes
     - Insurance
     - Denial of use (inefficiencies, unavailability)
     - Lost revenues

7. **Salvage Costs**

    Values of land, building, or building elements salvaged
     - Land
     - Buildings
     - Building elements

(Life cycle cost factors are outlined in more detail in Life Cycle Cost Analysis, A Guide for Architects, The American Institute of Architects, Washington, D.C. 1977, the original source for the information in this chart.)

Figure 3.3

An illustration of a life cycle cost analysis by a property management department is shown in Figure 3.4. The analysis examines whether a corporation in need of consolidating operations should renovate and add to an existing building or construct a new building on a different site. The analysis concludes that although initial construction costs for moving to a new site are higher than renovating and adding to the existing building, the total costs are lowest for this alternative over a twenty-year cycle. Similar analyses can be performed on alternatives to purchase or lease space.

Stage of Maturity

An important ingredient in overall property management strategies is the stage of maturity of an organization. A variety of property management options are available, moving from initial formation through growth, stability, aging, and eventual decline. Various elements of an organization may move through independent cycles of maturity, requiring separate subsets of property decisions.

Every organization goes through the following stages: Initial, Growing, Stable, Aging, and Declining (see Figure 3.5). In each stage, economic impacts are examined and various property management strategies applied. Capital costs for construction, and operating costs for staff and material, must be considered at each stage.

Growth in the organization occurs on a vertical axis and time on a horizontal axis. In the initial stages of an organization's development, leasing space is followed by decisions to either buy or build space. This is a critical stage for strategic planning of property management alternatives. A stable organization may be undergoing some expansion of space and alterations for changing organizational structure. Renewal and replacement of existing space may also occur. The aging organization faces choices of replacing obsolete facilities and major building components, or demolishing facilities. In a declining stage, decisions must be made for consolidating space by selling or leasing owned space, terminating leases, and/or demolishing marginally used facilities.

Other Factors

Other factors affecting decisions are:

- Government regulations for land use
- Environmental protection controls
- Occupational health and safety
- Handicapped accessibility

Management Issues

A checklist of property management issues for carrying out the responsibilities of buying, building, leasing, or selling, include the following factors.

Defining Specifications

The specifications for a property management transaction should be defined consistent with organizational goals and objectives. This is done by preparing an outline of the space requirements for building area and performance relationships, financial goals for investment and returns, and time schedules. Next, operational costs are estimated, including overall impact of staff, taxes, insurance, and other payments.

RENOVATE OR MOVE?

THE PROBLEM

The O.K. Corporation has an obsolete main office building of
50,000 gross square feet (GSF) on a crowded downtown site.
Additional office space of 50,000 GSF is leased on two separate
sites. Expansion opportunity exists on an owned parking lot
adjacent to the main office building. O.K. desires to
consolidate all operations into a modern facility. Some years
ago, a 20 acre site was purchased outside the city.

Should O.K.: (A) renovate and add on the the existing building?;
(B) demolish the existing building and build on this site?; or
(C) demolish the existing main office building, sell the
property, and build on a new site?

CRITERIA

A 20-year planning horizon and a 10% rate of return results in a
Uniform Present Worth Factor of 8.514 to find the Present Worth
of annual continuing costs (factors for other planning horizons
or discount rates are available from standard financial
references).

PROGRAM

Alternative A
50,000 GSF of renovations; 60,000 GSF of addition (a 10,000 GSF
penalty for inefficiencies in the renovation); a 300 car parking
garage to compensate for lost surface parking.

Alternative B
100,000 GSF of new space on the existing site; a 300 car parking
garage.

Alternative C
100,000 GSF of new space on a new site; a 300 car parking lot.

ANALYSIS

Figure 3.4

	ALTERNATIVE A RENOVATE/ADD	ALTERNATIVE B DEMOLISH/ REPLACE	ALERNATIVE C RELOCATE TO NEW SITE
INITIAL COSTS			
Renovation:			
Alt A: 50,000 GSF			
@ $30/GSF	$1,500,000		
New Construction			
Alt A: 60,000 GSF			
@ $80/GSF	4,800,000		
Alt B & C: 100,000 GSF			
@ $80/GSF		$8,000,000	$8,000,000
Sitework	50,000	50,000	300,000
Parking			
Alt A & B: 300 Car			
Garage @ $6,000/space	1,800,000	1,800,000	
Alt C: 300 Car Lot			300,000
Demolition	100,000	300,000	
Disruption Penalty	100,000	250,000	50,000
Other Project Costs @ 20%	1,670,000	2,080,000	1,730,000
Real Estate Income	100,000	100,000	200,000
TOTAL INITIAL COSTS	$10,120,000	$12,580,000	$10,580,000
ANNUAL CONTINUING COSTS			
Renovated Space			
Cleaning @ $1.50/SF	$ 75,000		
Utilities @ $3.00/SF	150,000		
Maintenance @ $1.50/SF	75,000		
New Space			
Cleaning @ $1.25/SF	61,200	$125,000	$125,000
Utilities @ $2.50/SF	150,000	250,000	250,000
Maintenance @ $1.25/SF	75,000	125,000	125,000
Functional Use Penalty	50,000		
TOTAL ANNUAL COSTS	$636,200	$500,000	$500,000
LIFE CYCLE COST ANALYSIS			
Total Present Worth of			
Initial Cost	$10,120,000	$12,580,000	$10,580,000
Total Present Worth of			
Annual Continuing			
Cost 20 years @ 10%=			
UPW factor of 8.514	5,416,607	4,257,000	4,257,000
TOTAL PRESENT WORTH	$15,536,607	$16,837,000	$14,837,000

Figure 3.4 (continued)

Space Utilization Review

An annual review of owned, and short- and long-term leased space allocation identifies space available for reassignment or disposal. The review process requires that a data file be prepared for owned, leased, and owned-leased space. Sample data files are shown in Figure 3.6 for a Property Control File, Figure 3.7 for Owned Property, and Figure 3.8 for Leased Property.

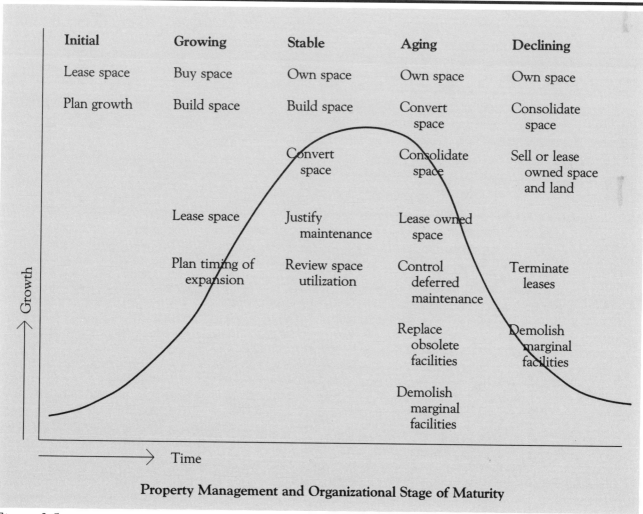

Initial	Growing	Stable	Aging	Declining
Lease space	Buy space	Own space	Own space	Own space
Plan growth	Build space	Build space	Convert space	Consolidate space
		Convert space	Consolidate space	Sell or lease owned space and land
	Lease space	Justify maintenance	Lease owned space	
	Plan timing of expansion	Review space utilization	Control deferred maintenance	Terminate leases
			Replace obsolete facilities	Demolish marginal facilities
			Demolish marginal facilities	

Growth ↑

Time →

Property Management and Organizational Stage of Maturity

Figure 3.5

REAL PROPERTY CONTROL FILE

Building Number	Building Name	Building Use*	Location Address	Ownership** Own/Lea/O-L
0001				
0002				
0003				
0004				
0005				
0006				
0007				

* Principal and Special Uses

** Own = Owned
   Lea = Leased
   O-L = Owned/Leased

Figure 3.6

REAL PROPERTY FILE - OWNED PROPERTIES

BUILDING DATA

1. Organization Name _____

2. Approved by
   Name _____ Title _____ Date _____

3. Building Number _____

4. Property Name _____

5. Property Address _____

6. Property Main Use/Special Use _____

7. Gross Area (Sq. Ft.) _____

8. Net Area (Sq. Ft.) _____

9. Type of Ownership: _____Owned

10. Book Value $_____ Year Appraised _____

11. Replacement Value $_____

12. Year Contructed/Major Additions _____

13. Year Acquired _____

LAND DATA

14. Type of Ownership: _____Owned

15. Book Value _____Year Appraised_____

16. Year Acquired_____

17. Size in Acres _____

18. Market Value $_____

NOTES:

_____
_____
_____
_____
_____
_____

Figure 3.7

REAL PROPERTY FILE – LEASED PROPERTIES

BUILDING DATA

1. Organization
Name _____

2. Approved by
   Name _____ Title _____ Date _____

3. Building Number _____

4. Paying/Collecting Department _____

5. Property Name _____

6. Property Address _____

7. Property Main Use/Special Use _____

8. Gross Area (Sq. Ft.) _____

9. Net Area (Sq. Ft.) _____

10. Size in Acres _____

11. Year Constructed _____

12. Lease Number _____

13. Date Acquired _____

14. Lease Start _____

15. Lease Expire _____

16. Indefinite Lease _____ (Y/N)

17. Annual Rent Payment _____ (Y/N)

18. Renewal Option _____ (Y/N)

19. Option Start Date _____

20. Renewal Period _____

21. Purchase Option _____ (Y/N)

22. Purchase Option Date _____

NOTES: _____
_____
_____
_____
_____
_____
_____

Figure 3.8

Government Regulations

Any real estate transaction is subject to one or more of the following government regulations.

- Zoning
- Environmental quality and land use controls
- Building codes
- Taxes
- Deed restrictions
- Energy conservation
- Occupational safety

Careful review of possible restrictions on a property transaction and compliance procedures can overcome obstacles which could impede timely meeting of goals and objectives.

Financial Impact

Real property activities (or inactivity) have a financial impact on an organization's debt and equity. The alternative choices for methods of funding require analyses of operating funds and debt capacity. Revenues and operating expenses must achieve desired returns and borrowing plans and fit into an overall financial plan. The impact of additional staff, maintenance, replacement reserves, and other costs involved in a transaction should be assessed by financial and legal consultants. Operations and maintenance staff or outside expertise should also be consulted when planning for buying, constructing, leasing, or disposing of property to determine overall financial impact.

Summary

Administration of property management requires performing tasks defined by policies and procedures, table of organization, and job descriptions. Each task—staff supervision; physical management of properties (cleaning, maintenance, etc.); financial controls and data management—should be related to overall organizational goals and objectives. The relationships between other departments should also be defined to ensure adequate performance by a property management department.

Chapter Four

FACILITIES PLANNING

From the moment an organization is formed, it engages in facilities planning. Facilities planning encompasses all the activities traditionally handled by urban planners, architects, landscape architects, engineers, interior designers, and other environmental design disciplines. Within facilities management, a planning department is established to analyze and manage the tangible fixed assets to best support the organization's overall objectives. For a government agency, facilities planning involves the determination of how facilities assets benefit the public. For an institution such as a college or hospital, facilities planning determines how buildings, grounds, utilities, and equipment support the basic missions of teaching, research, public service, or patient care. Facilities planning for a manufacturing firm determines how its facilities best support production, distribution, and service.

Basic Responsibilities

The basic responsibilities of facilities planning are:
- **Advising** on organizational policy for fixed assets
- **Coordinating** construction and space use with user functional requirements
- **Supervising** project management
- **Planning and designing** construction and space change
- **Consulting** on technical requirements for maintenance operations, acquisition of advanced technologies, and user requirements

Facilities planners may function in several or all of these roles, depending upon the stage of an organization's life, its size, and its traditions. In most organizations, however, facilities planners advise policymakers in addition to supervising construction projects and coordinating space.

Advising

The facilities planners' influence in strategic planning, property master planning, and project programming and design is directly proportional to management confidence. Therefore, to make full use of the planning branch, the staff must be competent and experienced. The facilities planner who is a talented and experienced architect can quickly grasp master planning issues and site-related building problems. When corporate officers and senior managers have confidence in the facilities planning staff, advice will be sought as early as the conceptual stages of projects. In these preliminary stages, a facilities planner conceptually evaluates whether alternatives of renovation, expansion, or new facilities meet senior management needs.

Advising senior management based on the results of feasibility studies on the alternatives for space needs is an example of a staff function. This is contrasted to operational tasks of project management for defined renovation or new construction projects.

Another advisory task involves assisting with the selection of consultants to advise on building site, architectural character, and functional requirements. Special consultants may also be required to perform economic and market analyses or for other unique facilities needs.

Coordinating

The facilities planner organizes the critical elements in the performance of a project and advises policymakers on the major decisions involved in moving a project from concept to occupancy. This includes coordinating consultants—making sure they are on the job at the appropriate times—preparation for public presentations, and funding. Funding sources must appropriately meet the financial needs of a project as it moves from the conceptual stages through design and construction.

Coordinating the processing of decisions through the fiscal and human resources of an organization is another task. Without such coordination, projects may: be delayed until all managers provide input, or lack the input of all senior managers.

Supervising

The supervisory task delegated to the facilities planning department is the delivery of attractive and functional building space on a timely schedule and within defined budgets. The chief facilities planner supervises staff, consultants, and project managers. The success of a facilities planning department can be measured by how well it maintains **quality**, **schedules**, and **costs**.

Planning and Designing

Projects managed by facilities planners have four phases: project planning and programming; design; construction; and post-construction. The elements of each phase are listed in Figure 4.1.

Judgments on the highest and best use of land and the aesthetic character of building projects should always be reviewed and influenced by facilities planning.

The facilities planner is the organization's **building project manager**. Project management may be supported by consultants, but overall project responsibility should not be delegated outside the organization. Acting as the owner's representative, the facilities planner must monitor each project to ensure that an organization's building program objectives are achieved.

Planning and Designing Responsibilities

Phase One: Project Planning and Programming

Analyzing:	The goals and objectives in acquiring or modifying space
	Alternative choices through feasibility studies
	Financial and human resources involved in the project
Programming:	Listing of space needs and functional relationships between spaces
	Relating the current space program to future needs
	Organizing the project team
Budgeting:	Project cost estimate
	Financing methods
Evaluating:	Summarize programming phase
	List professional skills required
	Present choices

Phase Two: Design

Land Use:	Site analysis
Design Concepts:	Form and interpretation of function
Schematic Design:	Design concept
	General scope and relationship of components
	Outline specifications
	Cost estimates
	Schedule
Design Development	Refined Design:
	Mechanical and electrical systems
	Furniture and equipment
	Construction materials
	Cost estimates

Construction Documents

Phase Three: Construction

Bidding
Contract Award
Construction Administration

Phase Four: Post-Construction

Project "Close-out"
Occupancy
Warranty Repairs

Figure 4.1

Consulting

The facilities planning department acts as a consultant within an organization, providing advice on a wide range of facilities-related matters, from implementing strategic plans to supervising construction. Space use problems, aesthetic improvement, and building maintenance problems should be reviewed by an organization's facilities planners. As with most planning tasks, requests for assistance are based on past performance and management's confidence in the facilities planning staff.

Providing advice to the operations and maintenance department is another type of consulting the facilities planning department provides. Close cooperation and respect from trade supervisors will encourage reporting of recurring or special problems outside of the worker's experience.

Reconciling differences between the people who prepare the blueprints and the operations staff is a routine problem in large organizations. Operations staff may feel certain problems were created by the designers of a building or system. Differences in individual's training and aptitudes should be recognized to gain the greatest use of operations staff's technical skills. Another solution in the large organization is to create a separate engineering group to serve the needs of operations and maintenance.

Departmental Structure

The organizational structure, size, and technical capabilities of a facilities planning department depend upon the overall plant size in buildings, area, and volume. The level of new construction, renovation, and interior space planning activities also influences the size and capabilities of a department. A single architect or engineer may meet the planning and design needs of a small or medium size organization, serving as an advisor to management, coordinator of space planning, and consultant to operations and maintenance. In contrast, large organizations with facilities in dispersed locations may require a planning branch at each individual site.

For organizations of all sizes, the facilities planning department should function as one unit directed by a single **chief facilities planner**. Sample job descriptions for the chief facilities planner of small and medium to large size organizations are provided in Figures 4.2 and 4.3, respectively.

Organizational Structure

Long range goals of strategic planning must be implemented by the skilled professionals listed below.

- Architects
- Landscape architects
- Structural and civil engineers
- Mechanical and electrical engineers
- Specifications writers
- Acousticians
- Cost estimators
- Architectural space programmers
- Interior designers
- Environmental health and safety specialists
- Telecommunications experts

Facilities planning is an integral component of the facilities management function. Therefore, it should be provided with the resources required to accomplish organizational goals. The capability of the facilities planning department to meet all of its delegated tasks depends upon the availability and qualifications of these skilled professionals to fill staff positions. Although the configuration of every company differs, the organization of a typical facilities planning department for a medium (500,000 to 1,000,000 S.F.) to large size organization (over 1,000,000 S.F.) is shown in Figure 4.4.

Consultants

The facilities planning organization may consist of staff, consultants, or a combination of both. Consultants are used to provide specialized talents and skills that cannot be regularly utilized or recruited by an organization. An advantage of using consultants is that they may provide objective opinions about facilities and building systems that are routinely overlooked by in-house staff. Disadvantages are that consultants can be costly and additional staff time may be necessary to orient outside professionals to a problem.

How and when to use consultants is ultimately decided by the chief facilities planner, although recommendations for consultants to supplement staff often come from department staff. The use of consultants should be balanced with available skilled permanent staff to ensure that project schedules can be achieved in the most efficient and economical manner.

Figure 4.2

Sample Job Advertisement for Facilities Planning Director of a Small Organization

General Description

The Facilities Administration Department of _____ is seeking an energetic, responsive individual to direct, organize, and manage the facilities planning division. The Director will be responsible for all architectural services, facilities engineering, and construction management. Applicant must have extensive facilities/maintenance experience. In addition, the individual selected for this position must have considerable knowledge of and experience in administrative and managerial skills including planning, design, estimating, construction methods, and scheduling. An ability to maintain effective working relations and strong communication skills are highly desirable.

Minimum Qualifications

Bachelor's degree in architecture or engineering and eight years supervisory experience in facilities management or an equivalent combination of education and experience.

**Sample Job Advertisement for Chief Facilities Planner
of a Medium or Large Size Organization**

General Description

The Facilities Planning Department of _____ has recently been established to plan the use and location of facilities; to improve internal coordination between planning, design, and functional user requirements; to upgrade the quality of facility design: to assimilate advanced office technology into facilities; to improve interface between furniture and space design; to plan, design, and evaluate all facilities renovations; and supervise construction management for adherence to schedules, budgets, and specifications.

The successful candidate will manage a department within the Office of Facilities Administration, which shall be accountable for:

1. Preparing a master plan for owned and leased facilities; determining immediate and future needs for facilities; and developing long-term space allocation, utilization, and management plans.
2. Supervising the design, project management, and evaluation of new facilities; developing the architectural terms of reference for bids; and establishing the standards and specifications for the purchase of office furniture, art, and accessories.
3. Supervising construction management to select methods of project delivery; construction awards; and construction administration.
4. Managing the human and financial resources of the department in a cost-effective and efficient manner.

Qualifications and Experience

1. B.S. degree or equivalent in architecture, engineering, or related discipline.
2. At least ten years experience as a manager in facilities planning, design, and construction coordination, including space and interiors planning, preferably related to large buildings and complexes (in excess of 500,000 S.F.).
3. Strong management background with proven ability to interact with all staff and management levels, provide leadership, and effect change in a new approach to facilities planning and design.
4. Experience in concept development; presentation of project proposals; development and monitoring of budgets and project scheduling; and development and control of work program.
5. Experience in development, implementation, and monitoring of standards necessary to ensure a consistent and cost-effective level of facilities design, project implementation, control, and evaluation.
6. Strong interpersonal and communications skills.

Figure 4.3

In-house staff should be regularly reviewed for technical competency to meet changing technical standards. When additional help is needed, the facilities department manager must decide whether to increase staff in size and technical ability, or hire outside expertise. The primary consideration should be to provide enough staff to support the basic mission of the organization. Other considerations of whether or not to hire consultants are:

- Is the staff size too small to handle the additional workload?
- Are staff too busy to meet the schedule?
- Is the need temporary or likely to continue indefinitely?
- Is special expertise required?
- Can additional costs be absorbed by the project?

In selecting consultants, project requirements must be considered as well as the organization's traditional practices. In addition, private and public clients alike should seek competitive bids when awarding consultant work to obtain the best possible assistance at the lowest cost. The American Consulting Engineers Council has published *A Guide to the Procurement of Architectural and Engineering Services* for evaluating and selecting consultant firms. Some general guidelines are shown in Figure 4.5. These guidelines are applicable to any design or construction management assignment, but should be modified to fit the special requirements of an individual project.

The consultant selection process is followed by fee negotiations and award of a contract.

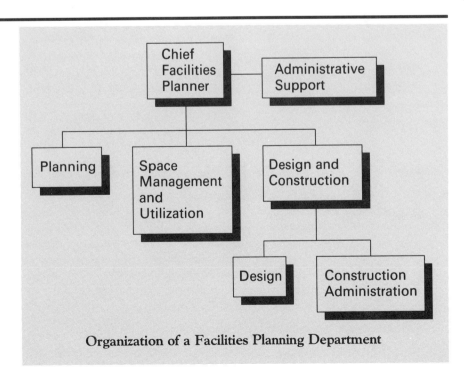

Organization of a Facilities Planning Department

Figure 4.4

Guidelines for Selecting Architectural and Engineering Consultants

1. The education, experience, and expertise of the consulting firm's principals and key employees.
2. The consulting firm's general experience, stability, and history of performance on projects similar to the one under consideration.
3. Availability of adequate personnel, equipment, and facilities to do the needed work expeditiously.
4. The name, or names, of individuals in the firm who will be assigned key project responsibilities, with particular attention to their qualifications, competence, and past performance.
5. The consulting firm's approach to planning, organizing, and managing the project effort, including communication procedures, approach to problem solving, data gathering methods, and evaluation techniques.
6. Facilities and equipment owned by the firm, including computer capability, reproduction and communication equipment, or other specialized equipment applicable to the project under consideration.
7. Present workload, as well as current and future commitments of available personnel, particularly those key persons expected to be assigned to the project.
8. Financial stability—Is the firm solely dependent upon the project at hand for its existence?
9. Recommendations and opinions from each firm's previous clients as to its ability to meet deadlines and remain within budgets. Prior clients may be able to advise as to the firm's sense of responsibility; attitudes of key personnel; concern for economy, efficiency, and environment; and quality of service.
10. On-site examination. If possible, observe each firm's facility and current and/or completed projects.
11. Proximity of the firm to the proposed project site and/or the plant administration's office.
12. The reputation of the firm within the profession and the community.
13. Awards received by the firm and technical papers authored by employees.
14. Special considerations for some projects might include staff conversant in foreign languages and qualified minority representation.

(This information has been provided courtesy of the American Consulting Engineer's Council, from A Guide to the Procurement of Architectural and Engineering Services)

Figure 4.5

Specific Duties of Facilities Planning

The specific duties of a facilities planning department for medium (500,000 to 1,000,000 S.F.) and large size (over 1,000,000 S.F.) organizations are: strategic facilities planning; design and construction; space management and utilization; energy management planning; telecommunications planning; cost controls; and management information systems. These responsibilities are outlined in Figure 4.6 and described in the remainder of this chapter.

Strategic Facilities Planning

Strategic facilities planning is an integrated process of developing alternate solutions for proposals based on organizational policies. The chief facilities planner advises senior management in the early stages of a project, when deciding whether to buy, build, sell, or lease property. In this role, the planner draws upon technical experience to sort out possible solutions and defines the tasks necessary to reach conclusions.

Another strategic planning responsibility is to provide solutions to specific requests within given sets of requirements. The goals may be generally defined or may be quite specific for space needs, budgets, and schedules of space availability. In such cases, prompt judgment must be made as to whether the tasks can be met by the facilities planning department staff or must be accomplished with the assistance of consultants.

Duties of the Facilities Planning Department

Strategic Facilities Planning
Physical Development Policy
Facilities Improvement Program
Capital Budgeting and Programming

Design and Construction
Project Planning and Programming
Project Design
Bidding
Cost Analysis
Construction Management

Space Management and Utilization
Space Standards
Space Inventories
Space Utilization and Allocation
Planning and Supervising Moves

Energy Management Planning

Telecommunications Planning

Cost Controls and Management Information Systems
Staff Budgets and Expenses
Projects Budgets and Expenses

Figure 4.6

One of the requisite characteristics of the chief facilities planner in strategic facilities planning is an ability to anticipate organizational facilities needs. The instinct to sense **when** and **what** may be required for new construction, additions, or renovations is enhanced by the facilities planner's understanding of the organization's resources and possible changing missions.

A strategic facilities plan is prepared under the supervision of the chief facilities planner. The purpose of the plan is to draw together principal elements of an organization's goals and objectives for facilities into a single reference document that is regularly reviewed and updated. The major elements of a strategic facilities plan include the following:

1. Physical development policy
2. Facilities improvement program
3. Capital budget program

An outline for a strategic facilities plan is shown in Figure 4.7 and described in the following paragraphs.

Physical Development Policy

The product of strategic facilities planning is a physical development policy. This policy is a statement that includes planning assumptions, project descriptions, and a program for meeting long-range goals. Broad guidelines for land use, vehicular/pedestrian circulation and parking, building and site design criteria, and infrastructure are described.

Facilities Improvement Program

All long-range plans for building construction, site development, and infrastructure improvement should be described in the facilities improvement program. This description should be concise, while containing enough information so as to be understood by other organizational components and funding sources. Adequate cost estimates and schedules should also be provided for use in reviewing project priorities.

Capital Budget Program

A capital budget program compiles all costs for facilities improvement and summarizes an organization's capital budget plans.

Space needs are first defined by feasibility studies for build, buy, sell, or lease alternatives. Choices are then translated into capital budgets consisting of cost estimates, schedules, and funding sources. Depending on the budgeting cycles (such as submitting financial plans to a funding authority), the capital budget is organized in annual programs within an overall five-year "rolling" planning period.

Government agencies and other organizations have formalized procedures for the submission of capital budget requests.

Design and Construction

This branch of facilities planning supervises the preparation of: the strategic development plan; feasibility studies and designs for renovations and new construction; contract documents; and construction management. These tasks may be performed by staff, consultants, or combinations of both.

Project Planning and Programming

Producing a design program is the first step in the design process for any type of construction or renovation work. The objective of the program is to define the scope of a project, including project description, budget, and schedule for completion.

Strategic Facilities Plan Outline

Physical Development Policy

Land Use and Site Planning. This category provides a summary of highest and best use of land indicating:

Existing buildings, new construction, and building additions

Future functional relationships on a multi-building site

Open space and future expansion needs

Anticipated acquisition of sale of land

Open space

Circulation and parking

Design Guidelines. Suggested criteria to be used as design guidelines for future building construction and site development:

Building form, heights, and volumes

Exterior materials and fenestration

Site furniture and plant materials

Building and site graphics

Vehicular/Pedestrian Circulation and Parking. Descriptions of functional relationships for vehicular and pedestrian circulation and parking. Included are site plans showing:

Site access

Vehicular circulation

Pedestrian circulation

Parking (surface and structure)

Infrastructure. Descriptions and plans showing:

Energy distribution systems (heating, cooling, electric)

Domestic water

Storm and sanitary lines

Natural gas

Telecommunications (voice, data, and other)

Facilities Improvement Program

Descriptions of building and site improvement projects with space allocations and functional relationships including:

Basic description of project

Site location

Outline space program

Cost estimate

Schedule

Funding source

Capital Budget Program

A description supported by tables for a multi-year program of capital improvements. A five-year program is the minimum suggested. Included are:

Project identification

Cost estimate (escalated to year of start)

Schedule

Funding sources

Figure 4.7

An organization should have formal procedures for obtaining descriptions of functional requirements and tentative schedules necessary for completing the design program, project design, and construction. The procedures are usually developed to fit the specific needs of an organization and provide documentation of the client's requirements. One method commonly used is interviewing the client to determine his needs and desires. Because of the inherent difficulty in expressing functional needs in terms of space, the facilities planner must be prepared to ask the right questions in order to shape a design program. When asking questions, one should avoid the temptation to ask for solutions to problems. The client should be encouraged to describe work activities and the relationships between these activities. A checklist of items that might be included in a client interview are outlined in Figure 4.8.

Using the feedback from the client interview on space needs and the nature of each activity, the facilities planner determines tentative space and volume requirements. Organizational space standards or guidelines are developed to establish standard square footage for each different function. When the space standards for program items or relationships are not obvious, special research may be required. This may include use of: available published sources such as Means *Building Construction Cost Data*; visits to buildings of similar types; or scale or full size models of the actual activities.

Defining a project budget is another task to be accomplished in the project planning and programming phase. The client may have a budget in mind that is unrealistically low for a costly design program. For this reason, it is important to establish a preliminary budget with adequate design and construction contingencies. Sometimes the exact budget cannot be determined until preliminary design studies are complete. However, an approximation should be made as a tentative budget using comparative data for similar building types. Cost references such as *Means Square Foot Costs* can be used for estimating a preliminary budget.

Once the project design program is completed, the facilities planner should review the program in detail and obtain approval in writing from the client.

Design Program Outline

1. Project Description
2. Activities and Functions
3. Circulation and Functional Relationships
4. Service, Storage, Parking, and Utility Requirements
5. Public and Private Spaces
6. Areas and Volumes
7. Special Equipment Requirements
8. Foundations and Structural Requirements
9. Mechanical and Electrical Demands
10. Safety, Security, and Maintenance Requirements
11. Finishes, Colors, and Furnishings

Figure 4.8

Project Design

Feasibility studies and conceptual or "preliminary" design may be necessary before decisions can be made to fund and proceed with construction documents. When the decision to proceed has been made, the project moves into detailed development of the design. This is typically done in the following three phases. Each phase is submitted to an authorized representative of the owner who is delegated the responsibility for approval. Approval of each phase is required prior to proceeding any further with the project.

1. *Schematic Design*: In this phase, the design concept, scope, and relationships of program elements are defined for client approval. A schematic, or conceptual, design includes enough detail of the architectural, engineering, and site elements for an evaluation of possible problems associated with funding, planning, and code review agencies.

Included in the schematic design are:

- Site plan
- Principal floor plans
- Site and building sections
- General project description
- Statement of probable project construction costs

2. *Design Development*: In this phase, the size and character of the project as a whole is established. Design development documents are based on the schematic design and, when approved, form the basis for the construction documents. Included are:

- Site plan, showing primary utilities, building parking, and landscaping
- Floor plans, elevations, sections, schedules, and notes to describe finishes, structural, mechanical, and electrical systems
- Outline specifications
- Construction cost estimates

Approval by the owner's representative at this stage "fixes" the design and accepts probable construction costs. Care should be taken for a thorough review before proceeding to the next phase.

3. *Construction Documents*: After design development documents are approved, the working drawings and specifications are prepared. Also known as bid documents, these include construction specifications and construction drawings. Specifications consist of Instructions to Bidders, General Conditions, Supplementary Conditions, and Technical Specifications. Technical Specifications describe the work in detail, the materials of construction, and the specific technical requirements of the completed work. Construction drawings provide graphic details of the work, the required dimensions of all elements of the facility, and an overall graphic representation of the work to be performed.

Small, uncomplicated projects to be completed in a short period of time may have a simplified set of bid documents. This may consist of several sheets of drawings, with specifications written on the drawings.

Bidding may also be simplified by using a document that includes: Solicitation of Proposal, Proposal by Contractor, and Acceptance of Proposal. Simplified General Conditions and Supplementary Conditions can be attached to this form.

Bidding

When the documents are complete, a choice must next be made as to whether the work will be accomplished by in-house plant forces or outside contractors. The availability of staff or the preference to use a contractor depends on schedules, project scope, and special trade requirements. If contractors are hired, contracts are bid and awarded by either the negotiated or competitive process. Several bidding strategies can be used: Lump Sum Fixed Price, Separate, or Guaranteed Maximum Price bids.

Lump Sum Fixed Price: Bids are submitted with a single sum for all work including site work, general construction, mechanical, plumbing, and electrical.

Separate Bids: Separate bids are solicited from subcontractors for each major section of the work. Management and coordination of the subcontractors may be handled by either the owner or a separately hired general contractor. The advantage in having the owner manage the work is that contractor's fees can be avoided, but requires that the owner's staff be capable of properly supervising the project.

Guaranteed Maximum Price: Competitive or negotiated bids with a guaranteed maximum price (GMP) are obtained from general contractors or construction managers before contract documents are completed. The major advantage of the GMP process is that the project can be accelerated because construction can begin before the final drawings and specifications are available. A contingency is usually required for this type of work because the information to the bidders is limited until documents are complete. This contingency can be reduced, but not totally eliminated, as the documents are finalized. The only modifications made to the GMP should be due to changes in the project scope or through opportunities carefully identified in the contract.

Cost Analysis

During design phases, the facilities planner provides project cost estimates.

Cost analyses may also be prepared by the facilities planning staff for feasibility studies or during development of concepts. Most often, architects or other consultants are contractually bound to provide cost estimates during the design phases. Value engineering for seeking economies in materials or construction methods can be provided by consultants during these phases.

The quality and reliability of these estimates are related to the progress of a design. As more detailed information becomes available, the estimate is assumed to be more reliable.

Contingencies may be added, depending on the stage of the design. The design contingency legitimately covers uncertainties in a project and may be reduced through each phase of the design. Contingencies should not be considered as opportunities for extra work or irrational budget reductions. When and how to use contingencies is carefully guided by the facilities planner to anticipate capital project costs. Cost publications, such as Means *Building Construction Cost Data*, are reliable sources of construction cost data. *Means Forms for Building Construction Professionals* provides a complete set of prepared forms which can be used for cost estimating purposes.

Standard methods of cost estimating are described in the following paragraphs.

Area and Volume Method: Comparative costs for similar projects are developed using costs per square foot. *Means Square Foot Costs* provides sample costs for a variety of building types, which can be adjusted to estimate average costs in a specific location.

In-Place Unit Method: This method is more accurate than the area and volume method. Construction components are counted and measured from the drawings. Typical components might include: lineal feet of interior partition walls, fire alarm systems, equipment, utility systems, or assemblies. A complete quantity survey in material units, such as thousands of brick, cubic yard of concrete, or board feet of lumber, is prepared, and labor costs added, to produce quantities for all direct construction costs. A price is obtained for each using contractor's prices or unit costs obtained from published references such as: *Building Construction Cost Data*, *Means Facilities Cost Data*, or *Means Assemblies Cost Data*. Additional amounts are added to the total for contractor's profit and overhead, and General Conditions. *Means Forms for Building Construction Professionals* provides preprinted forms which can be used for this method of cost estimating.

Construction Management

Traditionally, projects were administered by the facilities planning staff or architects. However, this traditional project management structure has undergone changes in recent years. Dissatisfaction by owners in cost and schedule control has led to the creation of a specialized field—construction management. Construction management is a method of project delivery in which construction work is supervised by a contracted professional construction manager. This service is ideal for the owner who infrequently builds major projects.

The construction manager can offer valuable input if consulted during the design phase of the project by offering value engineering suggestions. Economies can be achieved by specifying less costly materials or more efficient assembly methods in developing the design.

There are three alternative models for employing construction management services: design phase, construction phase, and management and performance of the work.

Design Phase: In this method, the construction manager is retained during the design phase to provide value engineering services as the design is developed. Cost estimates are prepared at each design phase and advice is provided to the design firm on economies to maintain the project budget. Services may or may not continue into the construction phase of the project.

Construction Phase: For this type of service, a construction manager is retained after construction documents are completed and then becomes responsible for managing the construction process. The construction manager supervises bidding, selects subcontractors, provides project coordination, and expedites the work.

In a "fast-track" project when a Guaranteed Maximum Price method is used, the construction manager becomes involved even before contract documents are complete, supervising initial construction while still coordinating the evolving final designs.

Management and Performance of the Work

This alternative to the above methods is one in which the construction manager is awarded certain phases of the work if he can offer a competitive bid. An owner or facility manager should be careful when determining appropriate fees for construction management services. Fees vary according to the size of a project. They are usually based on a percentage of the cost of the work, reimbursement of overhead, and direct expenses. Due to the complexity of contingencies, proposals from potential construction managers should include summaries of both fees and reimbursables, to avoid choosing misleadingly low fee proposals.

Space Management and Utilization

Organizations routinely "manage" space by evaluating use, reassigning for new uses, and reporting on space use for various purposes. New functions, expansion and consolidation, and accommodating new technologies all require space management.

Management and utilization of space includes:
- establishing standards for space use;
- inventory of existing space;
- evaluating space utilization;
- allocating space;
- planning; and
- supervising.

Space Standards

The use of space standards is fairly routine for architects and interior specialists. Criteria for interior space standards is empirical—data from past projects is accumulated to provide guidelines for various activities. There are several different types of space standards available for reference, including building codes, described in the following paragraphs.

Anthropometric Data: Human dimensions for males, females, adults, and children are illustrated in diagrams and with data. From this information, special standards can be developed to establish required dimensions for various activities. These dimensions can be used for planning layouts of aisle widths or other seating arrangements. A source of information is *Human Dimension & Interior Space* by Panero and Zelnik (Whitney Library of Design, N.Y. 1979).

Room Data: Dimensions for different types of rooms are provided in total square footage to be used as planning standards. This information allocates the space for a typical office, classroom, hospital room, or other function. An organization should develop a standard list of spaces and required areas for use in building design, interior space planning, or leasing evaluations. Available reference material on planning standards is in: *Time-Saver Standards for Building Types* by Chiara & Callender (N.Y. McGraw-Hill, 1980).

Activity Data: Data for typical uses such as auditorium seating, a basketball court, or truck loading is useful in planning new construction, renovations, or interior space planning. This data can be obtained in *Architectural Graphic Standards*, by Ramsey Sleeper.

Code Data: Other readily available references for space standards are local building codes. These standards ensure that building planning conforms with legal requirements for occupancy, health, and exiting requirements, but can be a source for planning standards.

Space Inventories

An organization determines the amount of space it controls and its characteristics through a space inventory. The inventory is compiled to determine: basic data for total building area; special space uses; and unique space characteristics. The data can be organized into lists of space to be used for planning purposes, management reports, and to meet external reporting requirements.

Computers can be helpful in storing historical data and producing reports. Calculations can be made for various elements if the computer system is programmed for that purpose. By recording and regularly updating the data on a computer, an organization has a readily available data source. Computer storage of this information saves time otherwise spent field-measuring spaces or entire buildings each time a planning or reporting need arises.

The basic element of a space inventory is **space**. This may sound simple, but inventories that do not aim to provide basic information on identifying a space and its characteristics can become unwieldy and useless. Manual or automated systems are available to perform calculations and generate reports.

At the very minimum, the following data must be provided for every space in the database:

- Space name to uniquely identify the space
- Physical dimensions of the space—length, width, or area
- Functional description of the space use
- The assignment of the space to a specific organizational unit

There are many other options which can be added to the basic data. Time and staff availability should be considered before developing lists of information desired in the database. Some items may seem interesting, but cannot be utilized practically. A clear concept of the inventory data that is absolutely necessary should be established to avoid gathering excessive and infrequently used information. Some suggested optional characteristics to include are:

- Height
- Equipment
- Floors
- Ceilings
- Walls
- Building cost
- Volume
- Ownership
- Initial occupancy date
- Lighting
- Air conditioning
- Occupancy capacity
- Telecommunications
- Replacement cost
- Latest improvement date
- Construction type

The space inventory is performed on a room-by-room basis, entered on worksheets during a field survey, and then totalled for manual tabulation or computer entry. Computer aided design and drafting systems (CADD) using digitizers can shorten this task.

Databases should be updated occasionally through field checks to ensure that an up-to-date survey is available.

Space Utilization and Allocation

Discretion about who and what goes into an organization's space can optimize a valuable resource. An organization's physical spaces are extremely valuable resources. Excessive space generates unnecessary costs. Insufficient or poorly utilized space can result in reduced productivity and higher operating costs. Proper utilization of space is a function of:

adequacy of initial size and layout; changes to number of occupants within the space; change in equipment or method of work performance within space.

In the small organization, space utilization should be regularly reviewed by visual inspection. A staff person is delegated to evaluate the efficiency and practical aspects of how well a space is being used. Personal comfort and operational requirements are the best guidelines for a common sense approach to utilization and allocation.

In the large organization, data is collected by a space inventory. There are two basic questions to ask in analyzing utilization:

- How much space is used for a person or activity?
- How frequently is the space used?

Average space standards must be known to measure utilization. For example, typical standards for classrooms use agreed upon measures of square foot per person and the number of times during a day and week a space is used. Present space usage should be compared to the standards for space per person and the desirable percentage of available time a space is in use.

The allocation task includes evaluating whether to increase or decrease the use of space to achieve the desirable standard. This decision requires judgment about the structure of the organization to group like activities together and make assignments. Preference for added space in certain locations should be balanced against functional requirements. Appropriate functions or departments should be placed in proximity to each other. If it is determined that all space is being used to its fullest capacity, and additional space is needed, plans should begin to add space or convert underutilized space.

Space utilization and assignment is critical to achieve the highest and best use of an organization's space. Each square foot of space is expensive to build and own. Debt service or lease payments, maintenance, and energy costs are ongoing during tenancy. In addition, an organization's morale is affected by the quality of the environment. For this reason, the facility manager should ensure that the appropriate amount of space is available for each person or activity, that workers are satisfied with their locations, and that employees feel responsibilities are being adequately rewarded with appropriate amounts of space.

Planning and Supervising Moves

Completion of a project usually includes coordinating the physical move by future occupants to the space. Occupants transferred from an old location to a new one usually bring along some personal possessions, equipment, and possibly even future furnishings. Advance planning can ensure that a move is accomplished smoothly.

Planning and Managing Interior Projects by Carol Farren outlines the following steps for a successful move into renovated or new space:

1. Specifications and bidding documents
2. Preparing the client for the move
3. Moving plans
4. Scheduling
5. Supervising the move
6. Clean-up

Energy Management Planning

Energy management means controlling the costs of conversion (from heat to steam, generating to power, etc.), transmission, and consumption. Energy management for facilities planners begins with advising on design considerations for renovations and new construction. Facilities planning may also provide recommendations for retrofitting old facilities, and establishing standards for monitoring energy consumption.

Because costs related to energy and environmental requirements can change rapidly, a strict list of conservation measures should be avoided.

Energy management guidelines for a facility should be based on a careful analysis of building occupancy and energy systems. Operating and maintenance guidelines for energy management specify design levels of energy consumption. Basic housekeeping, such as keeping heating and cooling sources clean and free of obstructions, maintains systems to operate at peak efficiency. For this reason, housekeeping measures for energy equipment should be regularly monitored to ensure that they are performed correctly at regular intervals.

Principles of energy management planning are summarized in Figure 4.9.

When **feasibility studies** are performed for purchase of new space, existing conditions and performance of utilities, mechanical, and electrical systems should be evaluated. Design requirements and operating costs for alternative systems should also be analyzed.

Energy Audits are another responsibility of energy management planning. Audits measure performance in terms of annual fuel costs or average consumption per square foot. The findings of an Energy Audit are used to determine where and what conservation measures can be made. Caution should be exercised when planning conservation measures to ensure adequate ventilation for occupied spaces and appropriate humidity levels.

The Energy Audit is performed similar to the Facilities Audit described in Part II of this book. The Facilities Audit can be amended to include an Energy Audit or modified to fit specific needs, using the following steps:

1. Select the energy management team.
2. Survey buildings for Energy Audit.
3. Tabulate present energy use.
4. Identify energy conservation opportunities.
5. Summarize costs and benefits.
6. Establish an energy budget.
7. Implement and monitor the program.

The database for an Energy Audit should include:

- Historical data on fuel and energy consumption and expenditures
- Explanation of rate systems and billing procedures
- Building system diagrams
- Building construction drawings and specifications.
- Operating characteristics of all energy-using systems for varied operating conditions
- Space operating conditions required by functional use

Three forms are suggested for use in conducting an Energy Audit. A Utility Consumption/Cost Survey Form (Figure 4.10) summarizes monthly data for a two-year period. An analysis of building functional areas identifies activities affecting relative energy load demands and is illustrated in the Building Load Survey Form (Figure 4.11). This form collects information on space loads and special characteristics of use,

Principles of Energy Management

1. Basic Principles of Energy Management are:

    System selection and operation specifically for building occupancy

    Energy use when and where required to provide minimum acceptable environmental conditions

    Minimize heat loss and gain

    Cost benefit analyses of systems and retrofit proposals

    Optimum operating efficiency for energy systems and equipment

    Regular energy audits to monitor performance and consumption

2. Energy Management for utilities depends on electric power and heat. Building utilities include:

    Electric power

    Heating and cooling

    Water supply

    Liquid sewage disposal

    Solid waste disposal

3. Conservation Factors—Lighting

    Efficiency of lighting fixtures and lamps

    Levels of illumination

    Economy in lighting use

4. Conservation Factors—Heating and Cooling

    Radiators and Convectors

    Keep heat transfer surfaces clean and free of obstructions.
    Install automatic control valves to individual units.
    Install a sensing device in building supply line with exterior-interior sensing device and night setback control.

    Fan and Coil System

    Avoid simultaneous heating and cooling.
    Reduce and balance water flow to minimum satisfactory levels.
    Shut off fans and let coils act as convectors when cooling and heating loads are minimal.

    Unit Ventilators

    Avoid simultaneous heating and cooling.
    Reduce and balance water flow to minimum satisfactory levels.
    Shut off fans and let coils act as convectors when cooling and heating loads are minimal.
    Limit ventilation to meet requirements and reduce when space is unoccupied.

    Single-Zone System

    Avoid simultaneous heating and cooling except as required for humidity control.
    Consider conversion to a variable volume system.
    Modify piping to use cooling coil for both cooling and heating.

Figure 4.9

Variable Air Volume (VAV) System

Limit air volumes to minimum requirements.

Install reset controls that regulate the hot and cold deck temperatures to demand and outside conditions.

Raise air supply temperatures so that the VAV box serving a space with maximum load is fully open.

Multizone System

Use automatic outside controlled reset of coil temperature and pump operation.

Achieve smallest possible temperature differential between hot and cold decks.

Dual-Duct System

Limit air flow to maximum extent possible.

Consider converting to variable air volume.

Raise cold deck and lower hot deck temperatures as much as possible. Reset according to outside conditions.

Close off ducts and shut down systems in response to demand and use a single-duct system.

Terminal Reheat System

Reduce air supply quantity as much as possible.

Raise air supply temperatures during summer months to the highest degree that will maintain satisfactory room conditions.

Adjust winter damper controls to raise air supply temperatures to the maximum to meet requirements without mechanical cooling.

Adjust reheat temperature according to outside conditions.

Induction System

Set primary air volume to original design values when adjusting and balancing.

Inspect nozzles for enlargement. If enlarged, adjust nozzle pressure to the appropriate setting.

Set induction cooling and heating schedules to minimum acceptable levels.

Reschedule cooling and heating water temperatures according to load and avoid simultaneous cooling and heating.

Shut down the primary air fans and raise the hot water operating temperature during unoccupied hours in the heating season to allow the induction units to operate as gravity convectors.

(This information has been provided by the Association of Physical Plant Administrators of Colleges and Universities, from Facilities Management: A Manual for Plant Administrators; Association of Physical Plant Administrators of Colleges and Universities, Washington, D.C. 1984, pp. IV 75-91).

Figure 4.9 (continued)

Utility Consumption/Cost Survey Form

JOB: HB & S Building

DATE: 9-9-88

Month Year	Elec 1 Kwh	Elec Demand	Elec 1 $	Fuel Gas mcf	Fuel Gas 1 $	Fuel	Fuel $	Degree Days-Htg
Jan '87	218671	623.2	9935	2061	3607			1006
Feb	225262	646.8	10130	2030	3553			894
Mar	307901	680.7	12749	1883	3295			679
Apr	339913	696.1	13613	1740	3045			132
May	385220	730.0	14837	1207	2112			0
June	403900	840.1	15341	1061	1857			0
July	456283	887.2	16756	990	1733			0
Aug.	461200	887.2	16888	1363	2385			0
Sept.	445450	865.0	16463	1526	2670			181
Oct.	385500	810.5	14845	1892	3311			761
Nov.	315630	721.3	12958	1691	2959			662
Dec. '87	216212	636.8	10274	2252	3941			1119
Total	4161142	887.2	164789	19696	34468			5434
Jan '88	212318	626.8	10168	1926	3370			974
Feb	208900	640.2	10076	2116	3703			912
Mar	316502	681.8	12982	2042	3574			603
Apr	341206	698.1	13649	1520	2660			261
May	402916	730.0	15315	1260	2205			0
June	400480	835.6	15249	1026	1796			0
July	482916	887.2	17474	1015	1776			0
Aug.								
Sept.								
Oct.								
Nov.								
Dec.								

Figure 4.10

Building Load Survey Form

JOB: __HB & S Building__   AREA: __Office__   WINTER: __75-30%__   SUMMER: __75-30%__   DATE: __9-9-88__

GLASS

Facing	SqFt	Shading Ext	Shading Interior	Type U = 1.13
N	1152	0	Blinds S.F. ~.64	Single
S	3608	0		Metal
E	4576	0		Casem.
W	5456	0		Avg. Fit
TOTAL	14792			

WALLS

Facing	SqFt	Shade	Type U = 0.20
N	8368	0	Light
S	4587	0	4" Brick
E	9464	0	4" Block
W	10609	0	Plas. Finish
TOTAL	33028		

ROOF OR FLOORS

SqFt	Type U = 0.20
10300	6" Concrete
	Built-up
	Roofing
	2x2 Lay-in Ceiling
10300	

LIGHTING / OCCUPIED / CUSTODIAL

Area	Type	Kw	Fc	Hrs/Wk	Kwh/Yr	Kw	Fc	Hrs/Wk	Kwh/Yr
Office - Exterior	2x4-200W Fluorescent	142.4	150	40	296192	142.4	150	20	148096
Office - Interior	2x4-200W Fluorescent	110.5	150	40	229840	110.5	150	20	114920
Halls	150W Incandescent Spots	21.6	40	40	44928	21.6	40	20	22464
Restrooms	2x4-200W Fluorescent	7.8	75	40	16224	7.8	75	20	8112
	TOTAL	282.3			TOTAL 587184	282.3			TOTAL 293592

PEOPLE / INFILTRATION

Area	No	Hrs/Wk	Infiltration Item	Crack Usage	Figure	Factor	Cfm
Office - Exterior	241	40	Doors	250 Pas/Hr	8-15	400	400
Office - Interior	181	40	Windows	14144 LF	8-14	.55	7780
						TOTAL	8180

DOMESTIC WATER

Use	Temp Hot	Temp Cold	Gal/Meals or Person	People/ Meals	Gallons Per Day	Btu/yr E6	Eff. Conversion	MCF/Yr
Handwash	110	60	3	422	1266	136.4	60 x 1	227

DISTRIBUTION LOADS

Item	Cfm	Gpm	Oa	Hp	Voltage	Amperage Rated	Amperage Opr	Kw	Hrs/Wk	Kwh Per Year
9-Exterior A-H Units	83500	456	8350	87.5	460/3	123	106	66.1	168	577450
8-Interior A-H Units	36000	216	3600	40.0	460/3	61	48	27.6	168	241100
2-Toilet Exhaust Fans	3200			1.0	230/1	8.5	7.5	0.8	168	6730

Figure 4.11

Distribution Load Survey Form

JOB: HB&S Building   AREA: Building   DATE: 9-9-88

Area Served	Item	Cfm	Gpm	OA	Hp	Voltage	Amperage Rated	Amperage Opr.	Kw	Hrs/ Wk	Kwh/ Yr
	CHW Pump 1		366		10	460/3	14	14	8.8	168	78877
	CHW Pump 2		366		10	460/3	14	14	8.8	168	78877
	Cond. Pump 1		450		15	460/3	21	21	13.2	168	115315
	Cond. Pump 2		450		15	460/3	21	21	13.2	168	115315
	Cool Twr. Fan				20	460/3	27	27	17.6	Auto	96096
	Boiler Fan 1				2	460/3	2.8	2.8	1.8	Auto	9828
	Boiler Fan 2				2	460/3	2.8	2.8	1.8	Auto	9828
	Elevator 1				40	460/3	56	Varies	Varies	40	16000
	Elevator 2				40	460/3	56	Varies	Varies	40	16000
	Elevator 3				40	460/3	56	Varies	Varies	40	16000
	Elevator 4				40	460/3	56	Varies	Varies	168	25000
	Dom Wtr. Pump				2	460/3	2.8	2.8	1.8	168	15725
	Chiller - 1		366		150	460/3	210	—	132	—	—
	Chiller - 2		366		150	460/3	210	—	132	—	—

Figure 4.12

76

occupancy, and exteriors. Information completing the basic survey is recorded on a Distribution Load Survey Form (Figure 4.12) to provide data on weekly and yearly energy consumption of specific equipment, such as pumps, fans, and chillers.

Telecommunications Planning

Planning for telecommunications was once a simple task. A call to the local telephone company and coordination of the electrical requirements to install or revise voice service were all that was necessary. Changes began to occur with the spread of computers and was compounded by divestiture of telephone service. It is now routine to include a telecommunications consultant in the design team for new projects. Telecommunications and data processing departments in large organizations may be responsible for overseeing staff and consultants performing these services.

Principal telecommunications planning responsibilities include:
- planning individual user needs and features for telephones, data terminals, video, signal, and other devices;
- coordinating inside and outside plant and power availability;
- supervising pathway installation and power connections; and
- maintaining pathway and telephone/terminal location plans.

The role of facilities planning in telecommunications is to provide careful advance planning to meet existing requirements and flexibility for future new systems. The rapid evolution of office technology, distributed data processing, computer systems, and combined voice and data systems indicate that telecommunications planning will continue to be a demanding task for facilities planners.

Voice and data transmission may be supplemented by video and voice signals within a building, between buildings, and to remote locations. A multi-building complex includes planning for "outside plant" of duct banks or direct burial of cable. Connections may be required for satellite dishes or other remote transmission devices on a permanent or temporary basis. "Inside plant" pathways for cable connections should allow for adequate flexibility for existing and future service generated from renovations and new construction. Adequate space is necessary for switching equipment at building entries and dispersed throughout a building.

The facilities planning department should monitor all outside and inside plant changes and maintain up-to-date site and floor plans in coordination with a telecommunications department. Changes in interior arrangements routinely require overnight alterations in locations of voice and data connections. For this reason, maximum flexibility should be provided by underfloor raceways, raised floors, or exposed overhead duct trays.

Cost Controls and Management Information Systems

Controlling costs for the facilities planning department includes managing staff operations and project costs. Staff costs, including personnel, equipment, and expenses, are budgeted centrally by the organization. Project costs are allocated from either operating budgets or capital budgets for individual projects, depending on whether they are to be capitalized over time. Approaches used must be coordinated with overall organizational financial management practices.

Data flowing to and from the facilities planning department is an important part of an organization's budget controls and cash management. Management information systems should be designed to conform with organizational needs for reporting on staff operating budgets and project expenditures.

Primary cost controls and management information systems for the facilities planning department are shown in Figure 4.13. (Staff budgets are explained in the following paragraphs. However, the remaining items in this figure are beyond the scope of this book.)

Staff Budgets and Expenses

Controls and management information systems for monitoring staff costs are similar to those used by professional architectural and engineering firms. Management information systems are tailored to fit an organization's budgeting, accounting, and reporting practices.

Facilities Planning Cost Controls and Management Information Systems

Staff Budgets and Expenses
Personnel
Contract Services
Equipment
Reimbursable expenses
Material
Space (leasing, utilities, etc.)

Project Budgets and Expenses
Site Work
Construction
Fixtures, Furnishings, and Equipment
Owner's Development Costs
Design Fees
Insurance
Legal
Telecommunications
Moving
Contingencies

Project Schedules
Staff Allocation
Design Phases
Construction Phases

Space Management
Facilities Audit
Space Inventory
Space Assignment and Utilization

Computer Aided Drafting (CAD)

Figure 4.13

The facilities planning department is generally budgeted centrally as an administrative service unit providing advice to the organization on all facilities matters.

Special arrangements within an organization may be used to charge certain services to individual projects. The question as to whether a facilities planning staff should be considered as overhead or accounted for as a direct project cost is frequently debated. Arguments favoring overhead treatment view facilities planning as a service department providing many different tasks that cannot be directly allocated to projects. One justification for including facilities planning in specific project costs is that all expenses related to individual projects are most accurately recognized. A choice should be made and applied consistently based on management's preference.

Means Forms for Building Construction Professionals contains preprinted forms for recording project budgets and expenses.

Summary

Facilities planning provides technical guidance in a wide range of activities. Included are guidance on strategic planning, design and construction, managing space utilization, and planning for energy management and telecommunications. Cost controls and management information systems support facilities planning and are integrated into the overall organizational practices and procedures.

A department staff may include professionals trained in urban planning, architecture, landscape architecture, interior design, and engineering. Other technical skills may be added depending on the size, number of facilities, and an organization's levels of activities in new construction, renovations, and space planning.

A facilities planning staff in a small organization (less than 500,000 S.F.) will provide a limited amount of contract document preparation for renovations and new construction. In the medium (500,000 to 1,000,000 S.F.) and large (over 1,000,000 S.F.) size organization, capabilities can be developed for preparation of contract documents and construction administration.

The facilities planning department is responsible for coordinating consultants retained to augment staff skills and availability. Finally, facilities planning provides technical advice for operations and maintenance.

Chapter Five

FACILITIES MAINTENANCE AND OPERATIONS

The facilities maintenance and operations department maintains an organization's buildings, grounds, utilities, equipment, mechanical, and electrical systems. The maintenance and operations department should provide timely, problem-free services to ensure a plant's continued operation in a safe, secure, and healthful environment. The department's services should enhance the appearance of the facility, while being as cost effective as possible.

The primary objective of the maintenance and operations department is to provide an acceptable environment in which an organization can accomplish its mission. The specific goals of maintenance and operations activities are listed below.

- Extend the life and improve the capability of facilities to perform at their maximum potential
- Reduce operating interruptions and equipment and structural failures
- Increase the productivity of operations and maintenance personnel
- Improve work methods and procedures
- Select the most cost effective methods of maintenance and operations, i.e., outside contracts vs. plant forces
- Reduce and eliminate fire and safety hazards
- Improve and maintain the aesthetic qualities of facilities
- Manage a control system that allows analysis and audit of the maintenance and operations functions
- Implement programs to conserve energy which comply with codes and regulations

See Figure 5.1 for an outline of responsibilities of the maintenance and operations department. Each of these responsibilities will be discussed later on in this chapter. First, however, it is important to understand the maintenance management terminology.

Maintenance and Operations Responsibilities

Maintenance Management Systems
    Building Inspections
    Work Planning
    Work Scheduling
        Preventive Maintenance
        Emergency Maintenance
        Routine Maintenance
    Work Task Completion
    Control and Reporting

Facilities Maintenance
    Preventive Maintenance
    Maintenance and Repairs
    Renovations and Minor Construction

Utilities Services
    Central Plant Operations
    Distribution Systems

Major Maintenance and Renovations
    Planning
    Design and Construction Documents
    Project Management

Grounds Maintenance
    Site Maintenance
    Interior Plantings
    Refuse Removal
    Equipment Maintenance

Custodial Services
    Standards and Staffing
    Work Scheduling
    Supervision and Training
    Equipment and Supplies
    Contract Services

Life Safety Systems
    Vertical Transportation
    Emergency Power and Lighting
    Alarms/Detectors
    Safety Equipment
    Hazardous Waste Removal

Energy Management Operations
    Systems Maintenance
    Inspections
    Scheduling
    Task Completion

Material Control
    Receiving and Distribution
    Control Procedures

Transportation and Vehicle Maintenance

General Services

Cost Controls and Management Information Systems

Figure 5.1

Definitions

Maintenance

Work required to preserve or restore buildings, grounds, utilities, and equipment to original conditions or such condition that it can be effectively used for its intended purpose is designated as maintenance work.

Emergency Maintenance

Unscheduled work that requires immediate action—to restore services or remove problems that could interrupt activities—is labelled emergency maintenance. Examples include: loss of electrical power, water, heat, or cooling; accumulation of ice or snow; and building failures representing hazards to personnel or equipment.

General Maintenance

Unplanned maintenance of a nuisance nature requiring low levels of skill for correction is known as general maintenance. General maintenance problems are usually identified and reported by facilities users. Examples are: replacing lighting lamps; adjusting door closers; repairing hardware; tightening plumbing connections; and lubrication.

Preventive Maintenance

A planned and controlled program of periodic inspection, adjustment, lubrication, replacement of components, as well as performance testing and analysis comprises a preventive maintenance program. Examples include: mechanical equipment; motors; filter replacements; emergency generators; cooling towers; and detection equipment.

Routine Maintenance

Routine maintenance includes repair or replacement of obsolete, worn, broken, or inoperative building components or systems. This type of work may be scheduled repetitive work or may be a request of a non-emergency nature initiated by a building user. Examples include: building repairs (masonry, hardware, glazing, painting, floor and ceiling finishes, etc.); grounds maintenance; equipment adjustments; and contract services.

Renovations/Modifications

This category of maintenance work describes changes to a basic facility or component to accommodate a new function. Renovation or modification work is initiated by a maintenance department or by the user. Examples include: reconfigurations of space to meet new requirements; modernization of space; and reducing operating costs of a facility.

Deferred Maintenance

Work that has been deferred on a planned or unplanned basis due to lack of funds in an annual budget cycle is known as deferred maintenance. Roof replacements, major building renovations, mechanical equipment, underground utilities, and roads and walkways are projects which are often deferred to the next annual cycle.

Organizational Structure

The organizational structure of the maintenance and operating department depends on the size, complexity, number of facilities, and an organization's traditional practices. The specific nature of the facilities to be maintained, required maintenance skills, levels of utilization, age, and condition of a facility also affect the organizational structure. Factors to be considered in selecting the most practical structure for a large organization are outlined in Figure 5.2. These factors can be modified for smaller organizations.

Before referring to specific examples of organizational charts for maintenance and operations, it should be noted that no two departmental structures are alike in actual application. Personalities of management and supervision, availability and capabilities of skilled trades, and unique assignment of responsibilities all affect the configuration of a maintenance and operating department. Relationships between organizational structure and staffing also depend upon management attitudes towards desired levels of maintenance and available funds.

The following organizational charts should be considered general guidelines for structuring a maintenance and operations department. These charts show the formal relationships between supervision and staff and should be supported by organizational procedures and job descriptions. The sizes of "typical" small, medium, and large maintenance organizations are provided below in ranges of square feet of space to be maintained.

Small Organizations

The small maintenance organization is defined as maintaining less than 500,000 square feet of space and with fewer than fifty employees (see Figure 5.3). A maintenance administrator reports to a chief financial officer. Support activities of accounting, personnel, and purchasing also report to this officer. Three basic functions report to the maintenance administrator: maintenance trades, grounds, and custodial. Cost controls are only partially handled by the department. Maintenance trades are responsible for carpentry, utilities, mechanical, and electrical systems. The trade supervisors perform planning and work control. In this context, specialized services are provided by outside contractors.

Medium Size Organizations

More complex department structures are required to manage a medium size plant consisting of a variety of facilities and activities. The structure of a medium size maintenance organization with less than 1,000,000

Considerations for Organizational Structure—Large Maintenance and Operations Organization

1. Number of facilities
2. Age and condition of buildings, equipment, and utilities
3. Location and dispersal of maintenance and operations work
4. Existing maintenance and operations organization
5. Procedures and practices
6. Complexity of building systems
7. Talent and skills of available managers and supervisors
8. Skill levels required and available personnel
9. Timing of work (determines shift hours)
10. Method of executing work (staff or outside contractors)
11. Availability and location of special equipment
12. Available communications systems

Figure 5.2

square feet of space and fewer than 150 employees is shown in Figure 5.4. An administrative unit headed by a facilities administrator has been added to this size category to handle maintenance management, some budgeting and accounting, personnel, and purchasing responsibilities. Work control and planning is performed by the maintenance staff.

Maintenance and operations for the medium size organization are divided into units for building trades, utilities, and minor construction projects. Preventive maintenance is usually performed by all of the operating units. As the maintenance department grows larger in size, it may be cost effective to add architects and engineers for design and construction administration.

Large Maintenance Organizations

The organization of the maintenance and operations department responsible for more than 1,000,000 square feet of space and more than 150 employees is shown in Figure 5.5.

The large maintenance and operations department is justified by virtue of an organization's size and available resources. A distinction of large organizations is that there are separate units for construction and engineering. When the organization is involved in the production, treatment, and delivery of utility services, a separate utility operating unit is also appropriate. A work control unit plans and schedules work to ensure greater efficiency, effectiveness, and reliability of the operating functions.

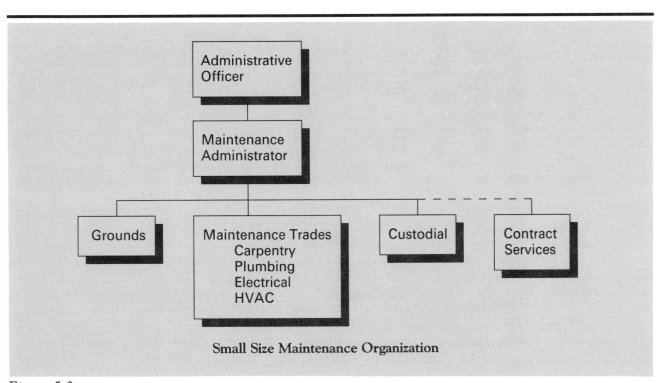

Small Size Maintenance Organization

Figure 5.3

Within this structure, the administrative support group provides budgeting, accounting, personnel, and purchasing services, in conformance with overall organizational procedures.

The construction branch, a full-time group of building trades staff, can be devoted to minor renovations, construction projects, and equipment installations. When a construction unit exists, its size and workload should be periodically evaluated to determine if maintenance activities are being deferred for the more rewarding construction work or if some projects can be performed more efficiently by outside contractors.

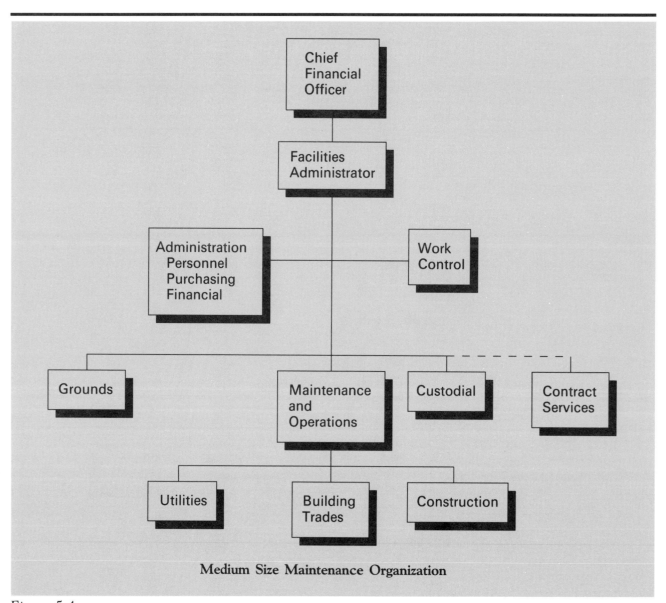

Medium Size Maintenance Organization

Figure 5.4

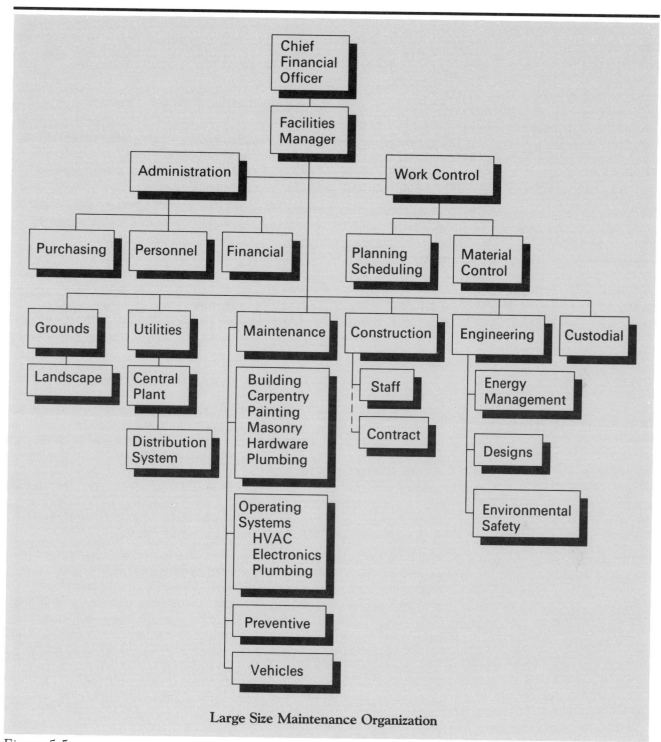

Large Size Maintenance Organization

Figure 5.5

An engineering function that complements a facilities planning department may exist in the maintenance and operations department of the large organization to readily provide technical advice on recurring maintenance problems and supervision of the construction unit.

Centralized or Decentralized Location

A final decision for the large organization is choosing between a centralized or decentralized staff.

The centralized department is usually organized into separate trade shops, each with a supervisor. Another alternative is grouping activities by the types of maintenance work performed, such as preventive maintenance, building maintenance, and minor renovations.

A decentralized department is managed by a single administrative unit with responsibilities at separate locations assigned to a supervisor and a team of craftsmen. Purchasing, accounting, and productivity measurement is retained centrally. Work control is supervised at the local level. It is usually more advantageous and cost effective to provide support for specialized skills and equipment from the central unit. Examples are the college campus or manufacturing company with dispersed activities over a large area. Advantages and disadvantages of centralized and decentralized maintenance organizations are outlined in Figure 5.6.

Staffing Guidelines

As the size, complexity, and dispersion of an organization's facilities increases, so does the need for more complex organizational structures. Budgeting, planning, scheduling, work supervision, and training eventually require a maintenance management staff dedicated to those functions. Performance of building maintenance, preventive and major maintenance, grounds maintenance, and custodial services evolve into separate units tailored to the purposes of the maintenance and operations department. Operating cycles, equipment performance, and concerns for a healthy, safe, and attractive environment dictate decisions on centralized or decentralized staff and contracted or in-house services.

Flexibility and adaptability are important in selecting the appropriate organizational structure and staff size for maintenance and operations. A maintenance management system should provide a core of staff and procedures. Budgets are translated into maintenance planning, scheduling, and work performance. A base of permanent employees—augmented by contractors—offers flexibility in completing emergencies, preventive and routine maintenance, and minor renovations. Adjustments in schedules for emergencies and new assignments can be readily incorporated under an effective maintenance management system. Adaptability is characterized by the ability to promptly and efficiently respond to changing requirements while sustaining normal workloads.

Staffing Levels

Staffing levels of a maintenance and operations department refer to the relationships between different levels of responsibility and the number and tasks of employees. For example, a base number of tradespeople requires levels of supervisory staff to appropriate direct work assignments. As the number and tasks increase, additional levels of supervisory and support staff will be needed to coordinate different functional areas and monitor work performance.

Some of the important principles to be considered in structuring levels and numbers are shown in Figure 5.7.

Centralized vs. Decentralized Organizations

Centralized

Advantages

1. Efficiency of administration and supervision
2. Larger talent pool for work assignments
3. Efficiency in dispatching staff, equipment, and material
4. Greater flexibility in staff assignments and daily workload
5. More efficient emergency response
6. Easier planning, scheduling and coordination of work effort
7. More convenient vehicle and equipment maintenance
8. Easier productivity and performance evaluation
9. Improved control and security of resources

Disadvantages

1. Increased transportation and communication expense
2. Less familiarity with individual facilities
3. Increased supervision requirements
4. More time required for productivity and performance evaluation
5. Increased emergency response time

Decentralized

Advantages

1. Opportunity for greater work productivity
2. Less travel time loss
3. Increased emergency response time
4. Closer supervision of completed work
5. Closer cooperation through a "team effort"
6. Familiarity with individual facilities problems

Disadvantages

1. Increased supervisory administrative tasks
2. Inefficiencies in planning and scheduling work
3. Expensive duplication of equipment and materials
4. Less availability of skilled personnel
5. Different levels of maintenance throughout the plant
6. Increased levels of communication required
7. Personnel absences have greater impact on work scheduling

Figure 5.6

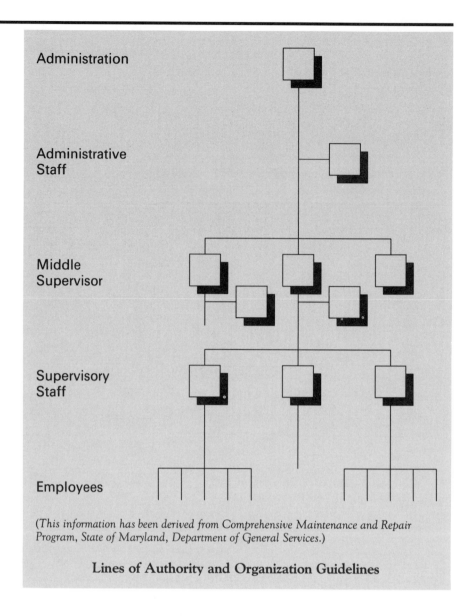

Administration

Administrative
Staff

Middle
Supervisor

Supervisory
Staff

Employees

(*This information has been derived from Comprehensive Maintenance and Repair Program, State of Maryland, Department of General Services.*)

Lines of Authority and Organization Guidelines

Figure 5.7

Lines of Authority and Organization: Some guidelines for structuring lines of authority and organization are listed below.

- Lines of authority should be clear and distinct
- Direct supervision should be limited to 5 to 7 employees per supervisor
- Vertical lines of authority should be as short and direct as possible
- Similar functional activities should be grouped together
- A manager or supervisor should be responsible for each functional group
- Assigned responsibility must be accompanied by appropriate formal authority
- Procedures are to accompany organizational guidelines

Administration: Administrative responsibilities involve planning and direction, both short and long range, for the maintenance and operations department in support of the overall organization. The administrators for this department include a Maintenance and Operations Director and assistant directors.

Supervision: Those charged with line responsibility for day-to-day supervision of maintenance and operations personnel consistent with administration direction and procedures are: middle supervisors for functional groups as required; and first line supervisors of shops or work groups.

Staff: Support staff assist all levels of the maintenance and operations department in performing their assigned responsibilities. Staff have no line organizational responsibilities. The number and size of support staff can vary greatly, depending on the overall size of the department. Staff positions include:

- Administrative staff
    Clerical
    Financial
    Technical
- Supervisory
    Work control and scheduling
    Technical and estimating
    Timekeeping
    Records control

Maintenance and Operations Craft Positions: Personnel typically employed to accomplish assigned work tasks include the following.

- Trade and craft mechanics
- Groundskeepers
- Vehicle and equipment operators
- Maintenance mechanics
- Fire and safety inspectors
- Operating engineers
- Housekeepers

Staff Size

There are no precise formulas to calculate the right number of employees. The guidelines presented here should be used to evaluate the size of an existing organization.

In general, a department should be no larger than necessary to meet continuing workload requirements. This can be established by performance measurements which gauge the responsiveness and quality of work performed. Monitoring the size of work backlogs can reveal over- or under-staffing situations.

Minor renovations and construction work can drain the resources of maintenance staff. However, for many types of services, contractors often prove more economic than building a permanent staff. Contractors can generally be used to meet specialized, periodic, or peak load requirements. Ideally, a balance should be struck between the number of employees from the highly skilled trades such as carpentry, plumbing, electrical, and other construction trades, and staff with lower level skills for general maintenance.

An illustration of staffing levels for various size organizations is shown in Figure 5.8.

Department Director

The director of a maintenance and operations department should possess some general qualifications, as well as have a specific knowledge tailored to the nature of an organization. The "general" skills include: prior administrative experience, and training in a technical area, such as architecture or engineering. Hospitals, colleges, and other entities have unique attributes that require familiarity through prior experience in similar settings. Experience in the military can sometimes be transferred to public or private organizations.

Maintenance and Operations Staff Levels
Number of Positions

	Facility Size (GSF)		
	Small	Medium	Large
Organizational Level	<100,000	<1,000,000	>1,000,000
a. Administrative	1	1	2+
b. Administrative Staff	1	1	2+
c. Mid-Supervisory	0	1	3+
d. Supervisory Staff	0	1	6+
e. First-line Supervisory	2	6	18+
f. Employees	8	50	149+
Total Positions	12	60	180+

Figure 5.8

Typical tasks performed by the maintenance and operations department director include:

- evaluating the continuing effectiveness of the maintenance and operations program and approving any changes in procedures;
- ensuring that all personnel are performing as required so that programs are running smoothly;
- preparing and submitting annual operating budgets;
- reviewing weekly performance reports and taking appropriate corrective action where required; and
- reviewing cost estimates for large maintenance requests and major maintenance projects.

Sample job descriptions for the department director for small (Figure 5.9) and medium to large size (Figure 5.10) organizations define responsibilities and qualifications.

Maintenance Management Systems

Maintenance and operations management departments that only respond to emergencies, face large backlogs of routine maintenance, and engage in occasional minor renovations are neither cost-effective nor very efficient. A maintenance and operations management system should be designed to increase the productivity of people and reduce costs. This section provides an overview of maintenance management systems. The reader is referred to Means *Facilities Maintenance Management* for a more detailed treatment of the subject.

Scope

A maintenance management system should include staffing, organization, and procedures for managing maintenance and operations through the processes of budgeting, initiating, planning, scheduling, executing, and reporting. Performance measures and cost accounting systems designed for controlling maintenance and operations efficiency and costs should also be included in the maintenance management effort.

Maintenance and Operations Director—Small Organization

General Description

The Facilities Administration Department of _____ is seeking a Maintenance and Operations Director. The position reports to the Vice President for Business and Finance. The primary responsibilities of the position include department budget and planning, and the management, supervision, and coordination of preventive maintenance programs, general maintenance, mechanical and electrical systems, custodial services, grounds, and other related support service operations.

Qualifications and Experience

Candidates should have at least five years experience in maintenance and operations administration and have demonstrated management skills. An ability to maintain effective working relations and strong communications skills are highly desirable. Candidates should possess a bachelor's degree, with an engineering degree preferred.

Figure 5.9

The following issues are regularly addressed by maintenance management:
- How much should be spent on routine maintenance?
- What is an appropriate staffing level?
- What is an acceptable level of work backlog?
- What is the appropriate response time to emergencies?
- How much maintenance labor and materials are allocated to minor renovations and construction projects?
- What is the right balance between staff and outside contractors?
- What is an acceptable level of deferred maintenance?

Maintenance and Operations Director—Medium and Large Size Organizations

General Description

The Facilities Administration Department of _____ is seeking an individual for the position of Maintenance and Operations Director. The Director reports to the Vice President for Facilities Administration and is responsible for the maintenance and operations of all owned and leased facilities, consisting of _____ buildings, (_____ million square feet), covering _____ acres. The Maintenance and Operations Department has an annual operating budget of $ _____ and a staff of over _____.

The Director manages the human and financial resources of the Department in a cost-effective and efficient manner. Areas of responsibility include budgeting and planning, building maintenance and operations, preventive maintenance, building renovations, energy management, vehicle and equipment maintenance, custodial services, grounds, and other related support service operations. The Director shall coordinate in-house staff and contractual management requirements in support of maintenance, renovation, and construction activities.

Qualifications and Experience

1. Bachelor's degree in engineering, architecture, business, or related fields.
2. At least ten years of directly related, progressively responsible experience in plant management, including significant experience as a senior facilities manager required.
3. Strong management background with proven ability to develop and control work programs, systems, and budgets.
4. Experience in development, implementation, and monitoring of standards necessary to ensure a consistent and cost-effective level of services.
5. Demonstrated capability to work under pressure and provide leadership.
6. Strong interpersonal and communications skills.

Figure 5.10

Work Control

Maintenance management systems assist in making decisions on these critical issues by **work control**—a systematic process for managing labor, materials, and work assignments. The larger the organization, the greater the need for a work control process that prepares work orders to assign tasks and monitor performance.

Cost accounting systems flow from the completed work orders, providing payroll information, material control, and accumulations of daily work into weekly, monthly, quarterly, and annual reports of expenditures against budgeted funds.

A work control center manages the flow of work requests initiated by maintenance and operations staff and consumers of services. Larger organizations require a staff of estimators, planners, and schedulers to manage information flows. Automated systems for accurately recording work requests, scheduling tasks, generating work orders, and monitoring results are invaluable tools for medium and large size maintenance organizations.

Functional Areas

The six major functional areas of maintenance management are organized in sequential steps—1) budgeting, 2) initiating, 3) planning, 4) scheduling 5) executing, and 6) reporting. Adjustments can be made in the sequence of these steps for emergencies and feedback on performance by the staff of each task. Predetermined procedures and policies are necessary for the six steps to define job responsibilities, routine documents, and create tools for evaluating performance. These areas are illustrated in Figure 5.11, and described below.

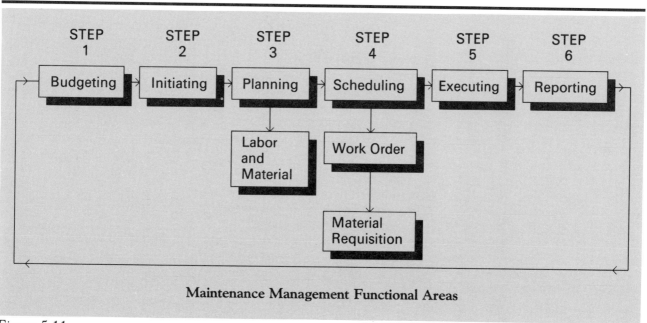

Maintenance Management Functional Areas

Figure 5.11

Step 1. *Budgeting*: In this step, annual funds required to maintain and operate facilities are estimated. In addition, actual expenditures are monitored by work type, building, and craft.

An overall operating budget must be estimated for labor, material, and vendors. Staff "benefits" should include all categories not collected elsewhere in accounting systems to provide an accurate picture of total maintenance costs such as social security, holidays, vacation, sick days, etc. In organizations using "charge-back" practices, all indirect costs of supervision, operating expenses, and equipment should be included in the total budget. A secondlevel of a detailed budget is produced for each craft, work type, and cost center where appropriate. Finally, quarterly and monthly budget worksheets are prepared for supervisory planning purposes.

The budget is prepared under the supervision of the department head, drawing on information from accounting and supervisors.

Step 2. *Initiating*: This means receiving and initially reviewing requests for work to be performed by tradespeople.

Requests for maintenance work are generated by several sources and transmitted to the maintenance and operations department in the following ways:

- **Unplanned work:** This type of work is user-identified. Unplanned work includes building and equipment repairs and failures and operational changes.
- **Planned work:** Preventive maintenance, seasonal work, routine and recurring maintenance, and custodial services are work items which are initiated, or planned, by maintenance supervisors and staff.
- **Inspection:** Facilities Audits, preventive maintenance reports, and code compliance inspections are initiated by management and supervisors.
- **Staff:** Management staff and other operating departments initiate tasks such as facilities planning and identifying facilities improvements.

The maintenance department should have a formal procedure for recording work requests. This system should also provide responses to requests for services to keep "customers," or the initiators of a request, informed on possible actions. Record keeping and regular communication with other departments helps to create favorable relations between maintenance and other organizational departments.

Services may be requested through telephone calls, written memos, and oral comments to maintenance supervisors and staff. Any information received should answer the following questions:

- **What?** What is the specific nature of the request for service?
- **Where?** The location of the service to be provided by room number, floor, and building number or name
- **Who?** The name of the person (the initiator) with a telephone number for future contact
- **When?** The date of a request and time desired for completion

A sample telephone log is illustrated in Figure 5.12 and a log for collecting staff comments is shown in Figure 5.13.

TELEPHONE RECEPTION LOG					
TIME	CALLER	BLDG LOCATION	DESCRIPTION OF WORK	ASSIGNED SHOP	WORK ORDER #

Figure 5.12

WORK REQUEST LOG				
REQUEST NUMBER	DATE	INITIATOR/ REQUESTOR	LOCATION	DESCRIPTION
001				
002				
003				
004				
005				
006				
007				
008				
009				
010				

Figure 5.13

As mentioned earlier in this chapter, work requests are controlled through a work order system, which is recommended for any size maintenance and operations department. Work flow may be managed and controlled by a **Work Control Center**, **Maintenance Operations Center**, or similarly named administrative support group reporting directly to the maintenance department director. Depending on the size of the facilities maintenance department, a work control group may include clerks, planners, estimators, and schedulers.

Step 3. Planning: Labor and material requirements are estimated for each work request in the planning stage. Planning also entails coordinating project staff for routine, emergency, preventive, and major maintenance requirements.

Work assignments are planned at different stages by the department director, supervisors, and maintenance mechanics. Managers are concerned with long- and short-range plans for the next one to ten years. Supervisors, or a work control group, direct the operating plans, assigning individual work assignments to the maintenance mechanics in the form of **Work Orders**.

In order to plan work assignments, each work task must first be prioritized. Prioritizing work ensures that tasks are scheduled according to available resources within the requested time for completion.

Maintenance priorities and definitions are listed below:
1. **Priority One—Emergency:** This work demands immediate attention. It may entail repairing an essential operating system or building component. Sometimes a task is prioritized as an emergency because life safety is endangered. Response for emergency work should occur within two hours of notification.
2. **Priority Two—Urgent:** Work demanding prompt attention to supplement emergency repairs, or a condition requiring correction within one to five days to prevent a subsequent emergency, is categorized as urgent work.
3. **Priority Three—Date Sensitive:** Often, a specific completion date has been requested or is required for certain work. The response time for this type of work depends upon the required completion date.
4. **Priority Four—Routine:** Work which has no short range effect on health, safety, or security of personnel or property is known as routine work. This work can be planned in detail and incorporated into the maintenance backlog for scheduling within thirty days of receipt.

Time estimates for each work task should be developed by supervisors and foremen. These labor estimates assist planners in estimating routine work requests. Guidelines for performing various maintenance tasks can be found in *Means Facilities Maintenance Standards*.

Complex maintenance tasks should be reviewed by planners and supervisors and, where needed, on-site inspections made to gather the necessary information prior to developing the time and cost estimates. Identified materials should be reviewed and ordered by supervisors prior to starting work to save additional time.

Step 4. Scheduling: This phase entails entering each work request into craft backlogs, determining the work to be performed daily by each craft, and preparing work orders.

Scheduling translates planning into work assignments. Schedules are organized based on employee availability on an annual, weekly, and daily basis.

Work orders are organized by priority and become part of the backlog for each craft. The backlog hours available for scheduling are computed weekly for each trade (see Figure 5.14).

Work orders should be reviewed with the craft foremen and supervisors and a weekly schedule established for each craft. These schedules are adjusted daily, as required, based on revised job requirements or other factors.

Weekly schedules for renovation or work requiring more than 24 hours of labor are based on productivity standards, either from a historical database or from cost publications such as *Means Man-Hour Standards*. Both the construction supervisor and craft supervisors should be notified daily of the anticipated man-hour requirements for each project.

Step 5. Executing: In this phase, requested work is completed by craft personnel or contractors under the direction of craft foremen or supervisors.

Executing the work assignment originates with the work order. Work orders are distributed to the foremen by the supervisor. The foremen direct the Work Orders to the appropriate craft personnel or maintenance mechanics. However, before delegating work assignments, supervisors and foremen should review the work orders and assemble material requirements to minimize job start-up delays. Foremen should visit job sites daily to ensure that quality work is accomplished and problems are resolved in a timely manner.

Step 6. Reporting: In this phase, periodic performance reports are generated that measure actual man-hours and materials against estimated man-hours and materials.

A reporting system begins with the collection of actual hours and materials used for each work order. This data is reviewed by supervisory personnel for accuracy to ensure that charges are accurately entered into the company's accounting system.

A variety of reports can be produced from historical data from past work orders to evaluate present performance on budgeting and work backlogs. Present budgets should be compared to the cost of past work to develop accountability for the workload. Finally, reports are developed providing expenditure comparisons and a year-to-date budget on a weekly, monthly, and annual basis.

Maintenance and Operations Procedures

An effective maintenance management system requires a procedures manual to ensure a consistent, controlled, and coordinated program. An outline for a Maintenance Operations and Procedures Manual is presented in Figure 5.15.

The manual should provide guidelines for: planning and control; budget management; inspections; trade coordination; emergencies; inventories; and work performed by contractors. Typical systems for each of these elements are described in the following paragraphs.

WEEKLY SCHEDULING WORKSHEET

CRAFT _____

OF PERSONNEL _____

SCHEDULER _____

	MON	TUES	WED	THURS	FRI	SAT	SUN	TOTAL
TOTAL CRAFT HOURS								
Less: Benefit Hours (@ 15%)								
TOTAL AVAILABLE CRAFT HOURS								
Less: Hours Reserved for Emergencies								
Less: Hours Reserved for Standing Orders								
Less: Hours Reserved for PM								
Less: Hours Reserved for Construction								
TOTAL HOURS AVAILABLE FOR SCHEDULING								
HOURS OF BACKLOG								
WEEKS OF BACKLOG								

COMMENTS _____

_____

_____

_____

_____

Figure 5.14

100

Maintenance and Operations Procedures Manual

1. General
Policies and Objectives
Staff Responsibilities
Maintenance Categories and Priorities

2. Planning and Control
Maintenance Planning and Control Concepts
Work Order System
Planning, Estimating, and Scheduling
Performance Evaluation
Inspections
   Types of Inspections
   Inspection Cycles
   Sample Checklists

3. Budget Management
Budget Preparation
Cost Accounting
   Maintenance
   Capital Projects
Financial Reports

4. Work Execution
Staff
   Regulations
   Overtime
Material and Equipment
   Purchasing
   Inventory Control
   Vehicle Use
Contractors
   Bidding Procedures
   Contracts
   Supervision and Contract Administration

5. Management Information System
Records
Reports

6. Health and Safety
Environmental Regulations
Protective Measures

7. Staff Training

Appendices
Standard Forms
References

Figure 5.15

Planning and Control

The type of planning and control system used by an organization depends on factors such as: the amount of space to be maintained; the location of the facilities; the availability of maintenance personnel; the capability of administrative and supervisory staff; and computer support. A properly designed and maintained planning and control system should accomplish the following tasks:

- Work order control
- Recording of requests for service
- Work priority identification
- Accurate data on availability of personnel, material, and equipment
- Work order system
- Adequate time reserved for emergency and preventive maintenance
- Flexibility for unexpected requirements
- Coordination by supervisors with building users

Budget Management

Budgets are prepared for an annual operating cycle to plan administrative expenses, labor, and materials. Cost accounting for each category, including contractors, provides data which can be used to estimate whether year-to-date activities are proceeding within the budgets.

Supervisors charged with budget responsibilities should participate in budget preparation and accountability for their areas. For this reason, supervisors should fully understand any special organizational formats and reporting procedures for budget preparation and monitoring.

Inspections

Periodic maintenance inspections of buildings and equipment should be scheduled and performed at least once a year. This procedure involves: scheduling personnel to perform inspections; providing instructions and forms to record inspections; and processing the results of the inspections into various reports.

Trade Coordination

Maintenance and repair work often employs more than one trade. Coordination between trades may take place in an informal discussion between personnel or could require designation of a project manager responsible for planning and scheduling, depending on the nature and complexity of the work. Written procedures should define responsibilities and actions to assure effective coordination of personnel, materials, and completion of the work.

Emergencies

Formal procedures should be developed to designate responsibilities and responses for emergency situations. Regularly occurring conditions such as weather, electrical failures, and heating system loss should have specific procedures and instructions. General procedures to cover unanticipated problems should identify minimum responses to emergency conditions.

Inventories

Inventory procedures should specify methods for control of a maintenance and operations department's material and equipment. Responsibilities, records, and control procedures should include requisitioning and accounting. Records should be kept for all equipment and should identify dates of inspections and maintenance work on all items in the inventory.

Work Performed by Contractors

Work performed by contractors should be guided by specific procedures for determining use of outside sources, bidding practices, inspection, and supervision. Bidding is usually solicited by department supervisors up to a cost limit for competitive and informational purposes.

Coordination of outside contractors with space users, and inspection of work, may be handled by a trade supervisor or construction administration group. Supervision includes adherence to contract documents and inspections for progress and final payments. As-built drawings and maintenance manuals for equipment should also be provided by the contractor before making the final payment.

Operations Management

Operations management includes maintenance, inspections, repairs, and replacement of building operating systems and equipment, central utility plants, and utility distribution systems.

Individual building systems should be considered as part of the building operation. Maintenance and operations of production and distribution systems are generally considered part of utility operations.

Advancing technology and sophisticated building systems require staffs that are technically able to perform the necessary tasks. A checklist of items handled by operations management is shown in Figure 5.16.

Organizational Structure

Organizational structure and supervision depend on the size of the plant, types, and complexities of operating systems.

Service contracts with outside firms are necessary for highly specialized equipment, especially in the small maintenance and operations departments where staff cannot be hired to meet around-the-clock service needs. Elevators, special power systems, and utility distribution systems fall into this category.

Organizational schemes may include mechanical and electrical shops as part of the maintenance trades group and a separate group for utilities. Medium and large size organizations tend to separate building maintenance from operations management because highly specialized skills are necessary to maintain certain pieces of equipment.

Decisions on the organization of operations must be based on the overall maintenance responsibilities and the availability of capable personnel.

Facilities requiring around-the-clock staffing and/or support from contractors, such as hospitals and residential colleges, demand close coordination between shifts and supervisors.

Energy Management and Telecommunications

Planning for energy management and telecommunications may be provided by a facilities planning department, or by outside consultants. The maintenance department acts as the installation, inspection, and maintenance staff for an organization's energy management systems.

Energy Management

Many organizations have recently recognized the need for energy conservation programs. The result is installation of energy conserving devices, building modifications, and monitoring systems. Introduction of energy conservation and cost reduction programs must be coordinated by the facilities planning department. Well-designed programs usually move from basic steps of sealing air infiltration, increasing insulation, and monitoring energy bills to more sophisticated programs.

Organizations in various stages of conservation programs may find it worthwhile to regularly review existing installations and new technologies that can improve conservation.

Checklist for Operations Management

1. **Building Mechanical Systems**
   Heating
   Ventilation
   Air Conditioning
   Plumbing
   Fire Protection

2. **Building Electrical Systems**
   Service
   Distribution Systems
   Lighting
   Emergency Power
   Telecommunications
   Security and Signal Systems

3. **Conveying Systems**
   Elevators
   Escalators
   Material Conveyors

4. **Central Utility Plants**
   Heating
   Cooling
   Electric Power Generation

5. **Utility Distribution Systems**
   Steam
   High Temperature Hot Water
   Chilled Water
   Electricity
   Domestic Water
   Natural Gas
   Storm and Sanitary Sewers

6. **Energy Management**

Figure 5.16

Energy audits should be performed on a regular basis to evaluate existing programs and the cost benefits of new programs. The audit provides data on energy consumption. Analysis can then be made of the energy use of specific buildings to determine high cost areas. The next step is to determine measures to reduce consumption.

Consultants may be of assistance in the overall audit process or in evaluating a specific proposal for energy conservation.

Energy management responsibilities include:
- Maintaining energy conservation programs
- Monitoring energy controls
- Analyzing utility bills
- Reviewing energy consumption
- Preparing reports

Telecommunications Systems

If an organization owns its telephone and data systems, installation, inspection, and maintenance services must be provided by in-house staff or retained consultants. Where capable staff can be hired, frequent training and updating of skills are necessary.

Telecommunications systems owned by an organization may vary from a privately owned telephone system limited to voice and data communications to a comprehensive computer switch and communications network. An integrated telecommunications system may even include a computer that acts as a switch for external and internal connections for transmitting voice, data, and video signals in the same pathways.

Outside a plant are connections between buildings such as pairs of wire, coaxial cable, or fiber-optic lines. Transmission in a telecommunications system may also include relay dishes mounted externally on buildings or on the ground. All of these elements of a telecommunications system must be regularly inspected and maintained.

The role of the maintenance and operations department is to maintain, install, and inspect the telecommunications systems. This requires highly skilled and regularly trained staff.

Coordination with any plant modifications to buildings or groundwork is necessary to avoid transmission interruptions.

Cost Controls and MIS

Cost controls for a maintenance and operations department depend on information available. Thus, effectiveness of management information systems is closely related to the way controls on personnel, materials, and equipment are exercised. Included are the costs for the following categories:
- **Personnel:** wages, salaries, and employee benefits
- **Materials and Supplies:** items consumed in administrative or maintenance and operations activities and not capitalized
- **Overhead:** charges for personnel, utilities, and material in support of maintenance work, e.g., administrative and supervisory staff, telephone service, utilities, etc.
- **Contract Services:** services of outside contractors, e.g., elevator maintenance, equipment service, construction, etc.

Control begins with budgeting and accounting procedures. Maintenance and operations budgets consist of expenses and revenues (where there are charge-back procedures for services) for immediate and long range maintenance objectives. Immediate objectives include routine and preventive maintenance, custodial services, and utilities. These are generally described in an annual operating budget. Long range objectives include renovations, repair, and replacement of major building and utility components such as: roofs; mechanical and electrical systems; distribution lines; and energy generating equipment. These are usually capitalized items and are described in a capital budget. Depending on the organizational structure, capital budgets may be managed by the facilities planning department with specific projects executed by the maintenance and operations staff.

Budget Preparation

Preparation of the annual operating budget for maintenance and operations follows the structure of a chart of accounts. A sample chart of accounts developed for higher education is shown in Figure 5.17.

Using a classification of accounts, the department director reviews each area of the budget from the previous year and evaluates whether to change maintenance and operations requirements due to modifications in total space, effect of renovations, or other functional space changes. The remainder of the process of organizing the annual operating budget is developed from labor and material estimates prepared by supervisory staff and compared to historical data. Total labor and material requirements for all types of work should be compared with current staffing and material expenditures. Adjustments for personnel costs due to compensation increases, changes in utility rates, and inflation should also be included in budget projections.

Cost Accounting

Cost accounting for the operations and maintenance department includes payroll records, material and supply purchases, and contract work. Procedures for maintenance and operations should follow those of the overall organization.

The work order system previously described provides basic information for payroll records. Additional payroll information includes vacation time, sick time, overtime, and other pay categories. Material and supply purchases are recorded by systems of purchase orders and invoices for payments. Using the framework of the work order system allows for the allocation of labor and material costs in a variety of ways. Costs can be defined by trades, buildings, and cost centers, and accumulated for year-to-date expenditures compared to budget categories.

Cost accounting for contract work follows procedures for purchase orders and payment invoices. Control of contract costs begins with the definition of services to be provided in an agreement. Construction work uses specifications and drawings to define the scope of work and methods of payment. Controls used for construction work are illustrated in *Means Forms for Building Construction Professionals*.

Management Information Systems

The basic purpose of management information systems for a maintenance and operations department is to have sufficient information for management to evaluate differences between budgets and actual costs and evaluate performance. The design of management information systems can vary widely depending on the extent of computer availability. A

Classification of Accounts

Administrative

    Personnel salaries, wages, and benefits
    Materials and supplies
    Telephone
    Computer services
    Postage
    Training
    Miscellaneous

Building and Equipment Maintenance

    Interior and exterior of buildings
    Maintenance trades
    Furniture and equipment
    Building utility and distribution systems
    Operating and replacement costs of all equipment, materials, and tools used in building maintenance

Custodial Services

    Personnel salaries, wages, and benefits
    Materials and supplies
    Operating and replacement costs for equipment used in custodial services

Utilities

    Personnel salaries, wages, and benefits
    Operation and maintenance of central plant(s)
    Operation and maintenance of utility distribution systems
    Costs for purchasing utilities
    Operation and replacement costs of utility production equipment

Grounds Maintenance

    Personnel salaries, wages, and benefits
    Maintenance of grounds and landscaping
    Maintenance of roads and walks
    Snow removal
    Maintenance of site equipment

Major Repairs and Renovations (Special Line Items)

    Personnel salaries, wages, and benefits connected with major repair and renovation projects
    Line-item special allocations and large improvement items
    Replacement costs of all equipment used in connection with major repairs and renovations
    Costs related to planning, design, or administration of major repair and renovations

Other Services

    Other essential services not consistently within the maintenance and operations department, yet frequently assigned are:
    Vehicle repair
    Construction planning and inspection
    Fire protection
    Safety and security
    Property insurance
    Solid waste disposal
    Trucking and moving

Figure 5.17

common pitfall of automating information for management is the production of masses of data that does not focus on key trend indicators such as comparisons of year-to-date expenditures to budgets for personnel, material, and outside contractors.

A work order system, either manual or automated, is a fundamental element of the management information system. Reports generated from labor and material expenditures can be compared to budget projections for annual, quarterly, and monthly periods. A weekly performance report should be prepared for all work orders to compare planned hours to actual hours for an evaluation of variances in performance. Planned ratios of materials to man-hours can also be compared for performance evaluation.

Performance evaluation includes manpower utilization and analyses of shop backlogs. Both of these subjects and computerized information systems for maintenance and operations are thoroughly treated in Means *Facilities Maintenance Management*.

Summary

The facilities maintenance and operations department maintains an organization's buildings, grounds, equipment, utilities, and mechanical and electrical systems. The primary objective of the department is to provide an acceptable physical environment for the organization to accomplish its mission. Size and structure of the maintenance and operations department is based on varied factors which should be given thorough consideration in development of an organizational structure, size of staff, and required tradespeople.

Decisions to be made for a maintenance and operations department are whether operations are to be centralized or decentralized, and the use of contractors for maintenance purposes.

Staffing the department includes selecting a properly qualified director, support staff, and supervisory personnel.

A maintenance management systems approach provides opportunities to increase productivity of personnel and reduce costs. A work control process that prepares work orders is a key element in the six functional areas of maintenance management: budgeting, initiating, planning, scheduling, executing, and reporting. A thoroughly prepared procedures manual is another factor that ensures a coordinated maintenance management system.

Chapter Six

FACILITIES SUPPORT SERVICES

The core functions of facilities management (property, planning, and operations) require services such as security and safety, telecommunications, parking and transportation, and mail services and distribution. These functions should be grouped under one management branch—facilities support services.

Creating a facilities support services department involves selecting those services with close organizational and functional relationships to facilities management. The underlying concept is that certain services support both people and facilities, with some services more closely allied to managing and operating facilities than serving people. Choices of location in the organizational structure for support services are usually in areas of financial, human resource, or facilities management. For example, a telecommunications department serves both financial and facilities areas. It would be placed in the facilities area if there was a particularly active period for planning and installing new, revised, or expanded telecommunications systems. If there was little change in the system, and coordination with facilities planning and maintenance was infrequent, the major activities would be business-oriented and the department located in the financial area of the organization.

The nature and size of an organization dictates the exact types of support services established. However, as an organization grows, these support services should be grouped under one supervisor to provide the highest levels of efficiency, cost-effectiveness, and communication. When these activities are grouped under one supervisory unit—facilities support services—they will be treated as a line department of equal status with other facilities management units. The advantages of this are direct access to closely related functional areas of similar levels of authority and responsibility.

The organization of a facilities support services unit is described in this chapter.

Organizational Considerations

Choices are made for the location of support activities in an organizational structure based on the following factors:

- An organization's overall space
- Number of buildings
- Operational practices and traditional alignment of functions
- Geographic location of facilities
- Convenience of control of dispersed facilities
- Resource limitations
- Legal requirements
- Quality of available management

The above factors influence senior management decisions in creating a facilities support services department, staffing vs. contracting for services, department size, and assignment in the organization.

Creating a Department

A support service may be initiated by a need to add staff for a specialized task, perhaps only one part-time person, either temporary or permanent. As the need expands to approximate a projected year's work, it may be cost effective to add a full-time employee. This additional work may be performed by a full- or part-time staff or by outside contractors. Increased demand for support services justifies creating a facilities support services department to perform the designated assignments.

An estimate of required staffing should be made after a review of the types of services to be performed and the desired levels of service. Consultants can provide guidelines for supervision, staffing, equipment, and procedures. These same guidelines can be used as specifications when soliciting competitive bids from outside contractors.

The justification for a particular support service department is based on the nature of an organization's business and whether the activity should be a formally organized operating unit. For example, if public services such as mail delivery can be handled adequately by the U.S. Postal Service, an internal mail distribution is unnecessary. Clearly, large quantities of print material between departments with priority distribution will require internal distribution. Another example is public safety—local public safety departments may provide adequate security and staff or contract services are not necessary. However, where risks to persons or property are high, staff or contract services may supplement an electronic security system.

Support service departments should be continually reviewed to reflect changes in the organization and its operating procedures. For instance, extended work hours in unsafe locations will require additional security measures. Introduction of new technologies in distributing information by facsimile machines or electronic mail may reduce the needs for mail or messenger service. Cost considerations also affect decisions—some inconveniences must be tolerated where there are limited resources.

Staffing Vs. Contracting

After the decision is made to create an operating unit, the next consideration is whether to hire permanent staff to provide support or to contract for services. Independent contractors argue that their services are less expensive and more efficient than in-house staff for the following reasons:

- Experienced, capable supervision
- Application of tested methods and procedures
- Management avoidance of labor problems
- Better buying power for supplies and equipment
- Pooling of a large labor source

Assuming that a contractor can perform equally as well as a staff person, these points should be given thorough evaluation prior to committment. The basic difference is that the contractor requires compensation for overhead and profit, in addition to labor costs. Retaining independent contractors also requires carefully prepared specifications and contracts, representing additional costs.

Means *Facilities Maintenance Management* outlines factors influencing the decision "when to contract for services": frequency of need; inadequate in-house talent; staff workload balancing; and other cost considerations. These factors are explained in the following paragraphs.

Frequency of Need: Certain support services are only required on a part-time or seasonal basis. In such cases, adding full-time staff may result in periods of inactivity or underutilization, and it would be best to contract for services.

Inadequate In-House Talent: Capability to provide specialized support services should first be based on availability of in-house staff. Training may meet this need without additional staff or contracted services. However, costs of training and retaining staff with new skills may exceed the overhead and profit costs of contractors. The local labor market for specialized skills also enters into the decision to hire additional staff or seek contractors.

Workload and Staff Balancing: An underutilized staff person may have additional responsibilities assigned to balance workload and avoid adding part-time staff.

Other Cost Considerations: Full compensation is often overlooked and only direct labor cost estimated in making judgements on staffing or contracted services. Contractors may provide lower costs by offering minimal benefits to employees. An advantage of contracting out to an "open shop" contractor may be possible avoidance of costs of an organization's own restrictive labor agreement. A disadvantage of using contractors is the possibility of reduced management flexibility caused by restrictive labor agreements with contractors. This can be a difficult policy issue and may be resolved by management practices and cooperative labor.

Security and Safety

Security and safety is a universal concern of all organizations. The degree of protection for life and property varies, depending on the complexity of an organization's facilities, equipment, location, and operational characteristics. These services may be provided in a tenant lease agreement or through support provided by another component of an organization.

Management's principal concern is that there are adequate policies and procedures in effect to protect life and property. Whether an organization operates its own department, contracts for services, or depends on local jurisdictions, its responsibilities should include:

- Maintaining a feeling of a secure environment
- Identifying and eliminating hazards and crime opportunities
- Providing protective patrols to deter and detect crime
- Detecting fire and safety hazards
- Minimizing risk of injury
- Enforcing organizational regulations and local and state laws

The development of an adequate security and safety department is initiated with an evaluation of the organization's demands and financial capabilities. For example, personnel and electronic surveillance and monitoring can be closely coordinated to produce cost-effective solutions. Existing cable plant may serve to provide connections between computers and electronic aids to central consoles. Central monitoring points supervised on-site or at remote locations can supervise electronic sensors, alarms, and monitoring cameras. They can also perform other security, safety, and equipment control functions. These types of opportunities should be thoroughly investigated when considering creating or expanding a staff, or retaining contract security and safety services.

Safety and security operations can be grouped under a single administrator or organized as two separate groups. The choice is based on the expanded needs for environmental safety caused by specific operations of the organization. Where there are potential hazards that require extraordinary procedures, a separate safety division is recommended.

Security

The decision to create a security department requires a firm committment to budgeting for administrative, personnel, and equipment requirements. The department focuses on security of life and property. Personal violence and burglary are supplemented by concerns for computer and "white collar" crime.

An organization has several choices in providing security services:

- Reliance on a public law enforcement agency
- Contracting for services
- Creating an in-house department

An adequate public agency is clearly the most cost-effective solution because additional funding is not required, unless a payment in lieu of taxes is necessary.

Contracting for services has the following advantages: readily available staff and support organization; eliminates hiring, replacement, and training; avoids personnel management. Disadvantages of contracting for services include: less quality control over employees; less familiarity with operational procedures and premises; lack of loyalty to organization; no control over discretionary release of information.

Organization: The director of a security department should be an experienced administrator with public safety or investigative experience, and be sensitive to the environment of the organization and its special operating characteristics. For example, the head of a hospital security department must be aware of the nature of emergency access for personnel on a 24-hour basis in a secure and safe environment. A service business may operate some activities on a routine work schedule and others on a round-the-clock basis. Understanding such unique requirements aids the director in establishing procedures, remaining flexible in directing operations, managing budgets, and staffing.

The director should have a good understanding of the civil justice system and civil liability processes. Judgment in responding to emergencies is also essential.

The size and make-up of the staff is based on the organization's needs and the director's observations. In some organizations, the security and safety department is the only unit operating on a continuous basis during nights, weekends, and holidays. Flexibility in balancing personnel and electronic monitoring devices creates cost-effective solutions for extended shift responsibilities and supervising dispersed locations.

Recruitment of individuals with minimum qualifications at entry level positions should be supplemented by an in-service training program. Familiarization with an organization's philosophy, policies, and regulations should be provided in orientations, on-the-job training, and special training classes. A security officer's basic role is that of observing, identifying, reporting, and, when necessary, apprehending. Therefore, it is essential to provide instruction in report writing, interrogation procedures, and the fundamentals of investigative techniques.

Policies and Procedures: The protection of constitutional rights must be reinforced by a policies and procedures manual. Consultants may be procured to help prepare this manual in conjunction with a director.

Departmental procedures, objectives, priorities, and internal controls are authored by the director and recorded in the manual. Minimum standards for performance and standard operating procedures should also be stated. Any changes in regulations should be approved by the director and reviewed by senior management of the organization and documented in the policies and procedures manual. In addition, provisions should be made for regular staff evaluations to assure that the desired levels of service are maintained.

A uniform reporting system should be established and supervised by the director. Records, files, and reports must be kept of statistics and financial information on a monthly and annual basis. Such documentation is useful in crime analysis, budget justification, and administrative oversight of the department.

A record and reporting system should include:
- Initial and follow-up reports on reported incidents and crimes
- Distribution of reports on a need-to-know basis
- Opportunity for inclusion in other public safety department uniform reporting systems
- Confidentiality of reports
- Permanent storage and ease of retrieval

Crime Prevention: One of the most important functions of the security department is to deter crime. An active program includes: dissemination of publications providing information on general and specific security problems; clearly posted security regulations and reminders of the need for personal safety; and lectures and seminars for the organization's staff.

Coordination with Other Agencies: Communication and cooperation with local public safety units is important to foster mutual understanding and promote mutual assistance. The local public chief security officer should be regularly informed of special conditions, especially those that require assistance. Agreements should be made with local jurisdictions and an organization's security department covering procedures that affect the organization's personnel or property.

Safety

A comprehensive safety department monitors an organization's occupational health and safety, to minimize health hazards and risk of injury. The physical well-being of personnel should be the primary consideration of a safety program. In addition, organizations are legally responsible for a growing number of federal, state, and local laws and regulations. An organization will benefit from a sound occupational health and safety program by realizing financial benefits through the prevention of injury, illness, loss of property, or interruption of normal operations and procedures.

A safety program should cover all aspects of an organization's activities. Appropriate standards should be established for each operation and facility, and procedures adopted to assure compliance with these standards.

The scope of an occupational health and safety program may vary widely but there should be provisions for the following:

- Policies and organizational structure
- Occupational health and safety standards
- Surveys and inspections
- Reporting, investigating, and record keeping
- Accident prevention
- Emergency procedures

Policies and Organizational Structure: A facilities management policy statement on occupational health and safety should be prepared and distributed to all employees. The policy should outline goals and objectives of the program and require the cooperation of all employees to adhere to applicable rules, regulations, codes, and standards.

A health and safety officer is responsible for administering the policy. This officer usually chairs a committee comprised of other department heads or designated representatives. In a large organization, staff may be assigned to the officer to help carry out inspections, investigating incidents, and maintaining records.

Hazards should be minimized in the planning phase rather than after construction or purchasing is complete. Regular coordination meetings should be held with representatives from security, property management, design and construction, maintenance and operations, purchasing, and risk management departments. This ensures that appropriate standards or codes are specified and that safeguards are included in construction, repairs, and purchase of property and equipment.

Occupational Health and Safety Standards: An occupational health and safety manual should be developed as a guide to safe practices and procedures. The manual should be approved by the organization's chief executive officer and regularly updated. It should include: the policy statement, references to applicable legislation and agency regulations, instruction for illness and injury reporting, and instructions for building evacuation and other emergency procedures.

Fire safety measures should be specified in the manual, such as placing maps on all building floors that outline routes of escape in case of fire. The manual should also include instructions on the storage and disposal of toxic materials and hazardous wastes, where applicable.

Government and industry standards should be considered minimums: it may be advisable for certain conditions to exceed these requirements. For example, higher rates of air exchange may be required to protect books or other print material. Higher HVAC standards are often required to protect sensitive material. Building standards should meet the needs of a particular facility, while providing a barrier-free environment, ventilation, illumination, fire and life safety, and first aid or emergency needs.

Standards for training in the safe use of equipment, the use of protective equipment, and correct emergency procedures should also be specified.

Surveys and Inspections: Facilities and equipment should be inspected upon acquisition and regular surveys of existing conditions taken on a periodic basis. Surveys should determine compliance with federal, state, local laws, and any special guidelines of the organization. Qualified personnel should conduct the surveys and record their findings in reports to the environmental health and safety officer. Copies should be forwarded to the supervisors of the area surveyed and to maintenance and operations for immediate corrective action. Surveys may vary from annual inspections to daily checks of hazardous areas.

Reporting, Investigating, and Record Keeping: The occupational health and safety department should establish procedures for reporting, investigating, and record keeping of accidents, injuries, and unsafe conditions and practices. Reporting enhances accident prevention effort; corrective actions can be developed from reports to eliminate unsafe conditions and practices.

Records of accidental injuries and illnesses provide information which is useful in identifying and analyzing ongoing problems and for program planning. The organization also protects itself in future legal actions by keeping records. Records can be used to determine the strengths and weaknesses of an accident prevention program.

Unsafe conditions are the primary focus of OSHA and EPA standards. Guidelines for identifying and reporting the presence of a hazardous condition and using hazardous materials should be developed and distributed to department heads and supervisors.

Accident Prevention Program: An accident prevention program serves an organization's objectives by identifying potential problems from reports and records. A program includes many of the items previously described: an occupational health and safety manual, standards, informational materials, and presentation. All personnel must be made aware of hazards throughout the workplace. Warning signs, signals, and notices should be understood and supervisors assigned to transmit such information to employees.

Safety in the environment requires safe working techniques and responsible behavior.

Emergency Procedures: Numerous emergency conditions—ranging from natural disasters and fire to threats of civil disturbance—can beset an organization and each one requires a special procedure. Emergency procedures should be developed which provide contingencies for various events. Such plans cannot prevent an emergency but can help mitigate its effects and minimize harm to life and damage to property.

An organization's emergency plans should be coordinated with local authorities and appropriate agencies. Regardless of size, organizations controlling their own facilities should follow some basic principles for impending emergencies. A chain of command should be established to define the authority and responsibilities of individuals. Responsible and knowledgable persons should be selected to make decisions in emergencies. Such individuals should have the authority to make modifications in procedures to respond to changing conditions. A control center for maintenance and operations should be established with a direct-line telephone bypassing the switchboard. Emergency power should be connected to the communications system. Equipment locations for items such as portable power generators, lights, and first-aid should be identified and regularly checked for seasonal conditions such as hurricanes, floods, or snowstorms.

An emergency manual should be written, and should include policies for the following conditions:

- Fire
- Hazardous environment
- Civil disturbances
- Hurricanes and floods
- Explosion
- Power loss
- Labor problems
- Snowstorms

Building evacuation plans are required for fires, explosions, hazardous atmospheres, and certain natural disasters. An evacuation plan should identify the following:

- Responsibility for activating the plan
- Training and practice requirements
- Special needs of handicapped persons
- Routes of evacuation and assembly points

Communications systems are an important part of emergency procedures. Periodic testing of alerting systems is required to ensure operational readiness and familiarity by all personnel. Alarm systems should be connected to emergency power systems. A careful survey should be made of all operating equipment requiring emergency power. Switching and alternate power sources are expensive and costs can be controlled by careful selection of equipment and circuits to be provided emergency power.

Telecommunications

The complexity of telecommunications systems has grown significantly beyond calling the telephone company for installations, changes in services, and paying bills. Organizations now typically have on-premise systems integrating telephone (voice), data, and video signals. Management of these services in a cost-effective manner requires knowledge and experience of a specialized nature. A facilities support services unit managing this function provides an organization with a central point for coordinating design, installation, service, and financial management.

Components of a telecommunications system are shown in Figure 6.1 and listed below.

- **Switch:** on-premise computer or local exchange service
- **Outside Plant:** cabling between building; aerial or underground
- **Inside Wiring:** building wiring connecting equipment
- **Terminal Equipment:** telephones, computer terminals, facsimile machines, monitoring systems, video displays

The system installed should be designed by an expert in the field, either a specially qualified department staff person or a consultant. Purchasing or expanding a system will depend on a careful study of communications, traffic patterns and volumes, and the requirements for capabilities other than voice transmission. For data, signal, or video, transmission quality

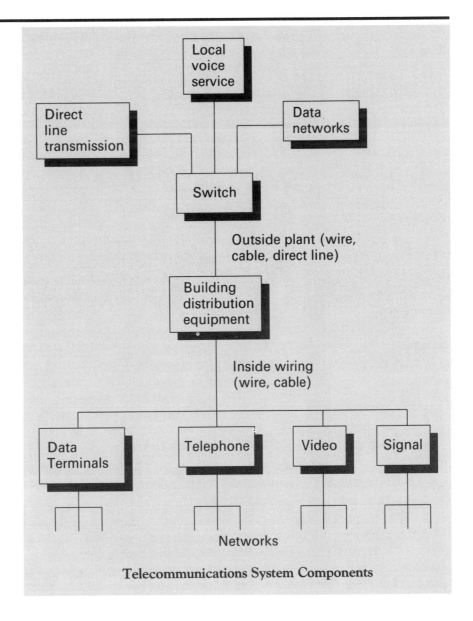

Telecommunications System Components

Figure 6.1

may be critical. Where certain levels of quality are not available on regular telephone circuits, fiber optic lines (owned or leased) may be required. Another alternative is a microwave system, although its high cost must be justified by high levels of traffic. If frequent transmission of exact copies of text or graphics are required, facsimile devices that transmit information over telephone lines may be used.

The responsibilities of a telecommunications department include:
- Budget planning and administration
- Telecommunications planning coordination
- Installation and maintenance coordination
- Inventories of cable plant, wiring, and equipment
- Billing analysis

Expansion or relocation of a department provides the opportunity to evaluate existing telecommunications systems and requirements. An in-depth analysis of past operations, plans, and forecasts should be made before making decisions for new telecommunications service and equipment. Such an analysis will ensure that appropriate, cost-effective service can be provided.

Information should be obtained from system users during this analysis. Information obtained from facilities users should include the items outlined in Figure 6.2.

Traffic, Parking and Transportation

The small organization in a leased space or a single building has relatively little concern for traffic, parking, and transportation. Adjacent land may be available to meet employee parking needs or nearby facilities may be available. Urban locations usually present acceptable parking facilities. Medium and large size organizations face more complex problems in controlling traffic, providing convenient and safe parking, and vehicular movement of personnel, materials, and equipment.

Organizations with buildings in a campus setting or within dispersed facilities require centralized coordination of traffic, parking, and transportation. A unit within a facilities support services department should be established to manage these functions.

Telecommunications Service Checklist
1. Responsibility of the department
2. Objective of the department
3. How operations are affected by telecommunications
4. Relationships to other departments
5. Urgency of communications
6. Physical arrangement of department
7. Number of people in department
8. Future long- and short-term plans
9. Special equipment requirements
10. Special operating requirements and conditions—handicapped service needs, noisy location, remote area, public access, and security

Figure 6.2

The impact of traffic, parking, and transportation on local services and the need for planning and budget management should be controlled for all of an organization's operations. Organizations managing these functions can decentralize some of the activities for enforcement by a security department and vehicle maintenance with a maintenance and operations department.

Consolidating traffic, parking, and transportation management under a single administrator enhances coordination of all modes of transportation and cost-effective solutions.

A tool for managing traffic is the **Transportation Systems Management Plan**, providing the most efficient use of transit service, optimum use of parking space, and options for different forms of commuting. The plan's goal is to use all resources for the most convenient and cost-effective solutions. A plan that serves employees, visitors, and other members of the served population, such as hospital visitors or campus students, reduces inconveniences and other common sources of dissatisfaction.

Traffic and Parking

Traffic and parking priorities should consider pedestrians, private automobiles, parking, and mass transportation. Pedestrians require barrier-free walkway systems; delineation of crosswalks; and police and traffic signals to control intersections. Private automobiles must be registered and identified. Service vehicles must be monitored for both access and restrictions on use. Planning is required for surface or garage structure parking and financing operations. Finally, mass transportation methods must be planned, including integration with public transportation, and owned or leased vehicles.

Planning for traffic and parking should be coordinated with the efforts of local agencies. Additional planning is necessary for events or situations which require special arrangements for traffic, parking, and transportation.

The organization in a campus setting or dispersed locations must provide convenient and reliable parking for employees, visitors, and service personnel. Planning for parking requirements should include consideration of present and future needs:

- Demand—number of vehicles generating traffic and parking
- Availability and value of land
- Land use development plans
- Surface parking vs. garage structure; financing, fees, and regulations
- Administration and enforcement procedures

Regulations for controlling vehicles and parking should be reviewed by an attorney and published for distribution among facilities users. An outline for traffic and parking regulations appears in Figure 6.3.

Transportation

Transportation responsibilities range from coordinating public transit service and employee and visitor needs to managing a fleet of automobiles, service vehicles, and mass transit (people movers, light rail systems, and buses). Organizational policies should balance economy and convenience, outlined by a Transportation Systems Management Plan. Transportation options should address the needs of all demands and traffic generators. Special attention should be made for the handicapped or mobility impaired.

A checklist of transportation options for the administrator to consider is outlined in Figure 6.4.

Outline for Traffic and Parking Regulations

1. Purpose and Objectives of Regulations
2. Authority—Legal and administrative basis enabling the organization to make and enforce regulations
3. Scope of Regulations
   Area regulated
   Persons regulated
4. Definitions
   Categories of permits
   Categories of use
5. Vehicle Registration
   Required registration
   Registration procedures
   Fees
   Insurance, title, and license requirements
6. Enforcement
   Responsibilities
   Penalties and payment procedures
   Penalty payments
7. Special Provisions
   Visitors
   Special events
8. Map
   Areas and facilities controlled
   Traffic routes and control points

Figure 6.3

Checklist of Transportation Options

1. Transportation Alternatives
   Purchase and operation by the organization
   Use of employee's vehicles with no reimbursement
   Use of employee's vehicles with reimbursement
   Establishing a motor pool
   Long term leasing of vehicles
   Cost-sharing with a public agency
2. Types of Vehicles Required
   Automobile
   Service vehicles (trucks, emergency, snow removal)
   Mass transit
   Airplanes
3. Vehicle Maintenance
   Organization maintenance facilities
   Contract services
4. Travel Policies
   Regulations
   Reimbursement
5. Motor Pools
6. Insurance Coverage

Figure 6.4

Venturing into the ownership of vehicles requires careful cost evaluations of differences between placing all of the burden for transportation on employees, sharing some of the burden with public transit, and/or reimbursement of expenses. The transportation administrator must weigh the costs for employee travel against the total cost of owning or leasing vehicles. Delays and inconvenience in travel for commuting between facilities or dispersed locations can cause employee dissatisfaction and attrition. A true cost accounting of owning vehicles includes the capital costs, operating costs—fuel, maintenance, and insurance—and loss of investment return of cash made for the expenditures. In the zeal to provide convenience and prerequisites, some or all of these considerations are often overlooked.

Mail Service and Distribution

Mail service and distribution involves the moving of printed information. Electronic messaging by facsimile machine and electronic mail is rapidly increasing but the moving of paper by personnel and equipment still remains as a required support service function. Mail and messenger service carry out this task. The basic activities are the collection, sorting, and delivering of inter-organizational, special carrier, and U.S. mail. Supporting operations may include bulk mailing, maintaining mailing lists, and providing inter-organizational messenger and delivery service.

The size of an organization and concentration or dispersion of facilities determine the staffing, equipment, and facilities for mail operations. Scheduling mail and messenger services depends on the volume and required response times.

Incoming U.S. mail and private delivery services are sorted and delivered internally on a daily basis. Collection from internal operations should be coordinated with U.S. Postal Service collections for timely movement.

A mail and messenger service is a labor-intensive time-consuming operation. Equipment that can increase productivity should be evaluated for cost-effectiveness.

Two considerations for mail and messenger service supervision are cost controls and security. Although for individual items unit costs involved are small, the total expenses of a department should be monitored to prevent abuses, and ensure careful metering of mail and packages. Only authorized personnel should be involved in mail processing, distribution, and collection because of the sensitive nature of some information and material.

Close liaison should be maintained with postal services to be aware of schedule and rate structure changes. Supervisory personnel should be familiar with U.S. Postal regulations.

Summary

Support services developed by an organization into departments may be appropriately aligned under facilities management. Examples are security and safety, telecommunications, parking and transportation, and mail services. Decisions on organizational structures are based on whether close coordination with facilities management improves efficiencies and is cost effective. Staffing a department versus contracting for services should be based on thorough accounting analysis and preferences for levels and quality of desired services.

Chapter Seven

COMPREHENSIVE FACILITIES MANAGEMENT

Each of the preceding chapters outlines assignments of administrative responsibilities to manage change and retain accountability. This chapter brings together the individual responsibilities described in Chapters 1 through 6 to provide a comprehensive view of facilities management. There are four major components to a Comprehensive Facilities Management Plan—the Strategic Facilities Development Plan, the Capital Budget Plan, the Facilities Management Plan, and the Maintenance and Operations Plan, as shown in Figure 7.1. Together, these components guide an organization in managing its capital assets.

Strategic Facilities Development Plan

An organization's strategic facilities development plan consists of policies and procedures for developing renovations, additions, and new construction projects. The plan ensures that the most appropriate facilities are available to support the mission, goals, and objectives of an organization:

- when needed,
- at an appropriate cost,
- in the right location, and
- at the desired time.

The elements of a Strategic Development Plan are: the Physical Development Policy, the Facilities Management Information Database, and the Facilities Improvement Plan. These elements are described in the following paragraphs.

Physical Development Policy

The physical development policy is an annually updated plan for five- and ten-year periods. The plan may be subdivided into smaller units of building complexes or geographic areas. A combination of narrative and drawings illustrate the plan's principle features for:

- land use and site planning;
- design guidelines;
- vehicular/pedestrian circulation and parking; and
- infrastructure.

The narrative should be concise and informative. Lengthy treatises of philosophies or planning jargon are unnecessary and will reduce the impact of the policy. Remember, the purpose of the Physical Development Plan is to bring together the key features of an organization's policies for guidance and ready reference. There should be an easily apparent connection between goals/objectives and each element of the policy statement. An example of part of a Physical Development Policy for a college campus is shown in Figure 7.2.

Facilities Management Information Database

A facilities information database has four components. The components are compilations of:

- existing facilities documentation;
- Facilities Audits of existing conditions and functional performance;
- space utilization; and
- maintenance and operations standards and performance.

Existing Documentation: All existing facilities documentation includes narrative descriptions, working and as-built drawings, specifications, surveys, property deeds and titles, operating manuals, and maintenance records. The material should be collected in a single location and given archival treatment for storage protection. Microfilming of drawings and duplicate copies of print material is advisable.

Comprehensive Facilities Management

A. Strategic Facilities Development Plan
   1. Physical Development Policy
   2. Facilities Management Information Database
   3. Facilities Improvement Plan

B. Capital Budget Plan
   1. Project Schedule
   2. Funding Sources
   3. Impact of Proposed Space Changes
   4. Project Priority Selection Guidelines
   5. Capital Project Programming and Budgeting

C. Facilities Management Plan
   1. Property Management
   2. Facilities Planning
   3. Facilities Operations
   4. Facilities Support Services

D. Operations and Maintenance Development Plan
   1. Organizational Plan: Facilities Planning and Operations
   2. Operations and Maintenance Policies Procedures
   3. Space Allocation Procedures

Figure 7.1

PHYSICAL DEVELOPMENT POLICY

Goals and Objectives
1. Campus Land Use Principles
2. Plan Components
*3. Land Use: Campus Core
4. Land Use: Residential Area - West Campus
5. Land Use: Residential Area - South Campus
6. Land Use: Athletics and Recreation

*3. LAND USE: CAMPUS CORE

The traditional campus core is defined by the ring road and the edge of the campus lake. Principal building uses proposed are for academic and administrative purposes. The Jones residential complex is to be converted to administrative offices and classrooms after new residence halls are completed in 1993.

All existing buildings in the main campus core are to be retained. A deferred maintenance program for 1990-1997 will renovate and refurbish the 12 major buildings.

Two structures are proposed on the north side of the campus core to complete the main quadrangle. Existing visual images and pedestrian circulation are to be reinforced by the siting, building mass, fenestration, and selection of exterior materials.

The main campus quadrangle is to be preserved as open space with vistas to the campus lake, protected by avoiding any future buildings sited in this area.

Figure 7.2

Facilities Audit: The physical condition and functional performance of an organization's facilities are assessed in a Facilities Audit. The purposes and procedures for a Facilities Audit are described in Chapters 8 through 11.

Space Utilization: Space utilization data assists facilities planning and maintenance, and operations with information on characteristics of space, occupancy, and frequency of use. Examples of the use of this data are in feasibility studies of alternative uses of space or in maintenance planning and scheduling to determine availability of a space for maintenance work and possible plans required to relocate an activity.

Standards and Performance: Finally, the facilities maintenance and operations function provides reports on costs of maintaining and operating facilities, maintenance deficiencies, and records of maintenance work as part of an overall building history. This information assists senior management in evaluating maintenance and operations performance and data useful to other facilities management departments.

Facilities Improvement Plan

A Facilities Improvement Plan provides the details for implementing the Physical Development Policies of an organization. Included are a priority listing and a description of individual major maintenance, renovation, and new construction projects.

The Facilities Improvement Plan is the "back-up" source of data for the Capital Budget Plan. The focus is on improvements and not budgeting decisions on sources of financing and assembling an overall schedule of all of an organization's capital projects. Careful attention should be given to providing the individual project description material to ensure that it is a reliable source of information. A word of caution: use of a project description later in a Capital Budget Plan may be the basis of funding and places an obligation on the facilities manager to provide the facilities as estimated.

A Facilities Improvement Plan requires a brief introduction describing contents, sources of information, and any definitions of terms that will aid the reader in understanding the contents. Project "schedules" are lists of projects by type and by priority, organized for ease of reference in preparing Capital Budget Plans. The content of a Facilities Improvement Plan, an outline of a suggested list of "schedules," and the contents of a project description are shown in Figure 7.3. A sample project estimate is shown in Figure 7.4.

A program of facilities improvement must recognize and address separately the differences between two important concepts; **capital asset management** and **functional improvements**. These concepts are too often mixed, which creates a confusing picture of an organization's overall capital needs.

Capital Asset Management: Restoring deterioration and extending the life of a facility are the objectives of capital asset management. Buildings, grounds, utilities, and equipment each have varying requirements for renewal, depending on individual life cycles.

In general, capital asset management includes preservation of building enclosures, structural frames, interior finishes, and mechanical and electrical systems. Infrastructure of roads, parking areas, electrical service systems, and central utilities are additional capital assets. Meeting life safety standards and compliance with regulatory standards, especially those required for a healthy environment (asbestos and PCB transformer removals, hazardous waste and toxic material control, and adequate building air circulation), are also aspects of capital asset management.

Protecting and preserving a capital asset requires maintaining plant condition, independent of a facilities' current or future use. Adequate capital reserves should be available to fund projects to reverse the aging process and correct deferred maintenance. Unfortunately, this is not always possible, as illustrated by the pervasive presence of deferred maintenance in many facilities.

Functional Improvements: Functional improvements enhance space to provide adequate facilities to meet the mission of an organization and reverse obsolescence. Occasionally, functional improvements will incorporate facilities renewal, either by major renovations or replacement of an obsolete facility.

A variety of facilities needs may be postponed because of poor financial planning or plant administrative decisions. For example, choices were made in higher education to reduce maintenance in order to fund academic programs, student life, or increase compensation.

Again, unclear distinctions and priorities between capital asset management and functional improvements blur definitions of overall capital funding requirements. The only method for accurately projecting plant renewal needs is by conducting a Facilities Audit—a detailed survey of facilities conditions including all building systems, components, and infrastructure. An audit can produce precise estimates of deferred maintenance and restoration projects. (Chapters 8 through 11 describe the audit procedure.)

Outline of a Facilities Improvement Plan

1. Introduction with a brief description of contents, sources of information, and definitions of terms, including criteria for priority selection.

2. Project schedules, organized by types of projects and priorities:
    Capital additions
    Repairs and renovations (over an established minimum limit)
    Deferred maintenance
    Functional improvements
    Energy improvements
    Regulatory mandates (local, state, and federal)

3. Project descriptions:
    Space program and justification
    Cost estimates
    Location and site plan
    Project schedule
    Construction delivery (traditional contract documents, fast track, construction manager)

Figure 7.3

CAPITAL PROJECT ESTIMATE

A. GENERAL INFORMATION

(1) Project Location _____

(2) Project Title _____ (3) Fiscal Year _____

(4) Project Description _____
_____
_____
_____

B. PROJECT BUDGET

(1) Project Development $_____

(2) Site Work & Utilities   _____

(3) Construction
    General Construction $_____
    HVAC & Plumbing   _____
    Electrical   _____

(4) Fixtures, Furnishings, & Equipment   _____

(5) Fees
    Architectural $_____
    Engineering   _____
    Reimbursables   _____
    Other   _____
                         _____

(6) Owner's Costs
    Surveys $_____
    Subsurface   _____
    Testing   _____
    Demolition   _____
    Utilities
     Relocation   _____
    Inspection/
     Supervision   _____
    Printing, etc.   _____
    Moving   _____
    Other Expenses   _____
                         _____

(7) Contingencies
    Design @__% $_____
    Construction
     @___%   _____
                                                _____

(8) TOTAL ESTIMATED COST (Date of Pricing) $_____

C. PROJECT SCHEDULE

	Bid	Constr	Constr	
Start Design	Period	Start	Complete	Occupancy

Estimate Prepared By _____ Date _____

Figure 7.4

128

When developing a Facilities Improvement Plan, the facilities manager must be cautious in distinguishing between "wish lists" and justified functional improvements.

Capital Budget Plan

A Capital Budget Plan outlines expenditures for new construction, major repairs or renovations, and major items of equipment. The principal sources of the Capital Budget Plan are items in the Facilities Improvement Plan. The Capital Budget Plan displays those projects selected from the different types of projects and summarizes annual funding and cash flow requirements for a specified period of time. Time periods vary from one to five years depending on an organization's budgeting practices.

The organization defines a **capitalized project** based on adopted accounting principles for various levels of value and expected life.

Capital and operating budgets should be integrated to determine the impact of facilities on needs for maintenance personnel, material, equipment, and utilities.

The Capital Budget Plan should begin with guidelines for the capital budget process and priority selection. This is followed by a description of project priority selection criteria. Next, projects are briefly described by title and graphically shown over the years to be carried out, with costs for each project year from planning through final payment (see Figure 7.5). Finally, a total of each year's expenditures indicates the organization's cash flow requirements, annual capital needs, and cash management strategies. Projects should be footnoted to show the method of funding. Supporting information can be provided with a one page summary for each proposed project, including cost estimates, schedule, and impact on operating budgets. These steps are summarized in Figure 7.6.

Facilities Management Plan

A Facilities Management Plan summarizes the organizational structure, functions, policies, and procedures of the components of a facilities management organization.

A concise and comprehensive plan is the goal. Each component should have a brief summary of the following:

1. Goals and objectives
2. Organizational structure
3. Primary responsibilities
4. Summary of operating procedures of interest to other operating departments

The introductory chapter of this book and the first six chapters provide background material for preparing the Facilities Management Plan.

Maintenance and Operations Plan

The Maintenance and Operations Plan is developed from the department procedures manual. A description of the manual contents and other information to be included in the plan are described in Chapter 5.

The plan should concisely summarize the goals and objectives of the department, organizational structure, and position descriptions, and policies and procedures of interest to other operating departments. Highlights should be emphasized in a brief condensation of the procedures manual. An outline of a typical Maintenance and Operations Plan is shown in Figure 7.7.

Capital Budget Plan—Project Summary

Year & Expenditures

Project Title	198x	198x	199x	199x	199x	199x	199x
1. Main building[a]	$000's	$000's	$000's	$000's			
2. Research laboratory #1[b]	$000's	$000's	$000's				
3. Roads and parking[c]		$000's	$000's				
4. Office building #2[d]				$000's	$000's	$000's	
5. Maintenance garage[e]				$000's	$000's	$000's	
6. Chilled water plant addn.[f]				$000's	$000's		
7. Mainframe computer[g]					$000's	$000's	
8. Land acquisition[h]						$000's	
9.							
10.							
11.							
⋮							
Totals	$000's	$000's	$000's	$000's	$000's	$000's	

Notes: [a]*Funding from property sale and operating budget*   [e]*Operating budget*
 [b]*Sale of bonds*   [f]*Capital budget*
 [c]*Sale of bonds*   [g]*Leasing/operating budget*
 [d]*Capital reserves*   [h]*Operating budget*

Figure 7.5

Outline of a Capital Budget Plan

1. Capital Budgeting Policies and Procedures
2. Project Priority Selection Guidelines
3. Project Title, Costs, and Schedule
4. Method of Funding
5. Impact on Operating Budgets
6. Supporting Information (a brief description of the project)

Figure 7.6

Outline of a Maintenance and Operations Plan

1. Maintenance and Operations Goals and Objectives
2. Organizational Structure
3. Position Responsibilities and Descriptions
4. Policies and Procedures for Functional Areas
   Budgeting
   Initiating
   Planning
   Scheduling
   Executing
   Reporting

Figure 7.7

The plan should also briefly provide guidelines for coordinating facilities planning and operations and maintenance. The overlap provided in this plan improves coordination between the two departments. An example is in the procedures for requesting services for minor renovations. Any modifications to structure, building mechanical and electrical systems, and life safety provisions should be referred to facilities planning for consultations before a work order is prepared.

Summary

Comprehensive facilities management brings together the components of an organization involved in the various aspects of managing facilities into a single administrative unit. Guidance is provided to the unit in a Comprehensive Facilities Management Plan consisting of four components—the Strategic Facilities Development Plan, the Capital Budget Plan, the Facilities Management Plan, and the Maintenance and Operations Plan. Each component is a concise statement intended for reference by the operating unit responsible for its preparation and other operating departments of the organization.

Part Two

THE FACILITIES AUDIT

A routine task of the facilities manager is answering the question: "What is the cost to maintain our facilities?" The Facilities Audit, explained in this part, provides a source for identifying the existing physical condition and functional performance of buildings, as well as its maintenance deficiencies. From the information collected during this audit, capital renewal and replacement requirements can be estimated for individual projects and annual forecasts. The Facilities Audit provides a basis for decision-making on routine maintenance, renovations, capital projects, and disposal of an organization's facilities.

Chapter Eight

INTRODUCTION TO THE FACILITIES AUDIT

Capital budget planning begins with compiling a complete inventory of the deficiencies existing in a facility. The Facilities Audit is a vehicle for producing such an inventory; it is a system for thoroughly assessing the existing physical condition and functional performance of buildings, grounds, utilities, and equipment. The results of this audit are used to plan major and minor, urgent and long term needs for corrective action, for short and long term financial planning.

The Facilities Audit is designed for use by facilities managers who oversee maintenance, capital renewal and replacements, and capital budgeting. The basic principles presented here can be applied to any scale operation, from a single structure to a facility consisting of multiple building complexes in dispersed locations.

Basic Structure

As stated above, the audit is a method of collecting information on current conditions of a facility. This information can be used to guide planning for regular maintenance and capital improvement projects. The audit is accomplished by evaluating the components of a building following the order in which a building is constructed.

The three basic phases of the audit process are shown in Figure 8.1. In this systematic approach, the scope of the audit is first determined. Next, the audit team is selected, and then a set of forms is designed. A survey team then records field observations on these forms for individual building components. Finally, the information from these forms is summarized, priorities set, presented, and used to:

- compare a building's condition and functional performance to other facilities.
- define regular maintenance requirements.
- define capital repair and replacement projects in order to eliminate deferred maintenance.
- develop cost estimates for capital repair and replacement projects.

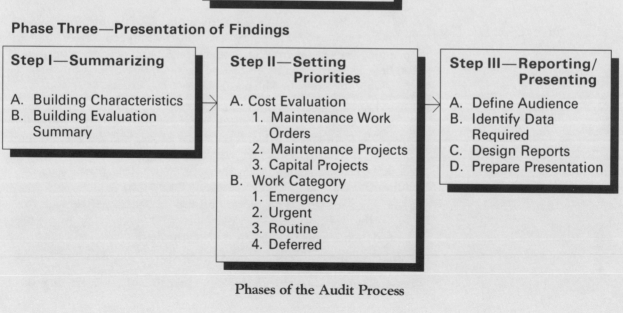

Phase One—Designing the Audit

Step I—Determining the Scope of Audit

A. What to Include
  1. Buildings
  2. Grounds
  3. Utilities
  4. Equipment
B. Depth of Audit
  1. Needs
  2. Cost
  3. Time
C. Methods
  1. Comprehensive Audit
  2. Condensed Audit

Step II—Selecting the Audit Team

A. Prime Responsibility
B. Members
  1. In-house
  2. Inter-agency
  3. Consultants

Phase Two—Collecting the Data

Step I—Designing the Plan of Attack

A. What information is to be collected?
B. Who will collect the information?
C. Schedule

Step II—Data Collection

A. Buildings
  1. Physical Data
    a. Primary Systems
    b. Secondary Systems
    c. Service Systems
    d. Safety Standards
  2. Functional Performance
B. Grounds
C. Equipment
D. Utilities

Step III—Data Evaluation and Analysis

A. Physical Evaluation
B. Functional Performance
C. Facility Rating
D. Project Cost Evaluation
E. Project Priority Ratings

Phase Three—Presentation of Findings

Step I—Summarizing

A. Building Characteristics
B. Building Evaluation Summary

Step II—Setting Priorities

A. Cost Evaluation
  1. Maintenance Work Orders
  2. Maintenance Projects
  3. Capital Projects
B. Work Category
  1. Emergency
  2. Urgent
  3. Routine
  4. Deferred

Step III—Reporting/Presenting

A. Define Audience
B. Identify Data Required
C. Design Reports
D. Prepare Presentation

Phases of the Audit Process

Figure 8.1

136

- restore functionally obsolete facilities to a usable condition.
- eliminate conditions that are either potentially damaging to property or present life safety hazards.
- identify energy conservation measures.

Uses of the Audit

The audit produces a database on the condition of a facility's properties, identifying the physical adequacy of construction, material, and equipment, and assessing the functional adequacy of the facility to perform its designated purpose. This inventory can be used to guide property management decisions, and strategic planning of capital assets, such as determining those assets necessary to extend the life of a facility.

The audit should be designed and analyzed in a systematic manner. If the audit materials are presented in a comprehensive, easy-to-use format, they:
- can be used in the field without extensive training.
- can be used without, and outside of, consultant assistance.
- can be used at any location, regardless of size.

Capital Asset Management

A comprehensive audit using the rating forms presented in this part of the book is one element of a systematic approach to managing an organization's capital assets. This enables better planning of maintenance and capital expenditures. Frequently, limited funds are allocated for new construction or levels of maintenance that impose long term penalties for inadequate design or deferring of maintenance. The result is facilities deterioration and excessive funds for future remedial work. Therefore, it is necessary to have one tool, the Facilities Audit, that clearly identifies and quantifies the condition and functional adequacy of the physical plant and the cost of various options for correcting deficiencies.

Elements of a strategic capital asset program are listed in Figure 8.2.

Future Audits

Although some information may be collected and analyzed by maintenance staff to ensure the working order of a facility, it typically does not include planning data needed to assess long term needs. The audit goes beyond maintenance planning. By following the audit procedures, a database of information on facilities is produced that can be used as a base line for future surveys of conditions.

The Rating Forms

The audit approach is, essentially, a thorough inspection of a facility. There are no shortcuts. The audit is a systematic process of methodically completing individual forms for each component following the way building components are assembled. This is a **self-evaluation process** designed to fit all types of structures. The audit procedure described is a "generic" approach that can be used as a starting point; the facilities manager should incorporate the special characteristics of an organization and its facilities into an individualized Facilities Audit.

As experience with the format of the rating system accrues, the facilities manager will see the merits of the system, that it results in a concise list of specific actions and alternative methods for restoring and maintaining the physical and functional adequacy of the facilities.

Content of the Forms

The self-evaluation process reports the physical condition and functional performance of a facility on a set of sixteen facility rating forms for building components and two functional performance forms. Each of the component rating forms contains four sections that provide:

- a record of building characteristics;
- system evaluation;
- comments on identified work tasks;
- a numerical rating for the facility.

The system evaluation section contains space for recording cost evaluations and priority ratings for work tasks.

Elements of a Strategic Capital Asset Program

1. **Property Database:** a property inventory with key factors describing land and buildings

   Facility name or number
   Location
   Use—main or special
   Gross area
   Type of ownership
   Value—book or replacement
   Age—original and additions
   Net area

2. **Physical Condition Audit** with analysis by components (see Chapters 8 through 11)

   Primary systems
   Secondary systems
   Service systems
   Safety standards

3. **Functional Performance Audit**

   Suitability for current use
   Historic value
   Social and community value
   Adaptability for future use
   Aesthetic value

4. **Selection of Priorities**

   Estimating costs
   Priority criteria
      life safety
      building deterioration
      functional improvements

5. **Facilities Management Plan:** an integrated action plan for maintenance and capital expenditures with projected:

   Budgets
   Time schedules

Figure 8.2

The evaluation of facilities using this method may be limited to ratings which are translated into replacement cost estimates of individual projects, or expanded to include detailed cost estimates and field identification of priorities for a facility.

The facilities manager is encouraged to become thoroughly familiar with the overall process before launching into the building inspection phase. A rereading of this material may be useful during the course of the inspection and preparation of report summaries.

Types of Forms

There are three types of forms used in the building audit to offer maximum flexibility in meeting an organization's needs. These are listed and described below. These forms are further explained in Chapters 9 and 10.

Facilities Inventory Forms: This form is designed to collect the basic data of an organization's building characteristics (name, identification number, location, area). This form may also serve as the master schedule for the audit.

Comprehensive Audit Forms: Inspections of building conditions and functional performance can be recorded on these forms. Comprehensive audit forms provide condition ratings and options for reporting maintenance deficiencies and cost estimates. Findings from comprehensive audit forms can be converted to estimates of capital projects using cost data from publications such as *Means Facilities Cost Data* or a replacement method for building components (described in Chapter 12).

Condensed Audit Forms: These forms are designed for organizations with limited resources in need of an abbreviated survey. This survey is limited to gathering data on maintenance and capital projects only. These inspection reports can be readily converted into work assignments and project costs for short term operating and capital budgeting.

Exceptions

A problem which may have to be settled by the audit leader is what to do with **mixed use buildings**, those which have **recent additions** to the original construction, or those buildings which have, under emergency circumstances, been **forced to house new activities** for which they were not designed. Such problems will have to be dealt with individually by the audit team.

Frequency of Inspections

The data gathered in a Facilities Audit must be kept current, gathered consistently, and then regularly updated. An annual cycle of inspections is recommended. Each organization initiating a comprehensive audit and continuing with annual cycles of inspections will benefit from organizing data in a systematic format. This ensures that evaluating and recording existing physical conditions and functional performance are worth the effort.

Methods of Evaluation

Forms are designed for ease of field entry of data and manual preparation of summaries and reports. The concepts can be applied to basic word processing and spreadsheet software or database programming. Although the self-evaluation process is readily adaptable to data processing programs, the capabilities or resources are not always available. For organizations without computer capabilities, a manual method of storing and updating must be developed and used.

Summarizing the Audit Data

Information collected on the audit forms is summarized and used to determine the condition of the buildings and what should be done to maintain and/or improve them. (This subject is explained further in Chapter 11.) Summaries of a building audit can serve several purposes. Some of these are listed below.

- **Routine Maintenance Needs:** A current property owner may be interested in planning a program for routine operations and maintenance.
- **Major Maintenance:** A current or prospective property owner may want to evaluate major maintenance needs to plan a corrective program.
- **Deferred Maintenance:** A backlog of routine and major maintenance may use a survey of conditions to plan a deferred maintenance program.
- **Renovations and/or Additions:** Prior to developing feasibility studies on alternatives to renovations and/or additions, a survey of existing conditions may be necessary.
- **Capital Budgeting and Planning:** A comprehensive audit of facilities conditions will incorporate major maintenance requirements into overall capital needs.

The individual Component Rating Forms provide:

1. System or component description
2. Component evaluation, including
    condition rating
    cost estimates to correct deficiencies
    priority ratings
3. Maintenance deficiency comments
4. Component rating

The information from the Component Rating Forms is summarized on a Building Evaluation Summary Form, which provides:

- a description of basic building information;
- a component rating summary; and
- a building rating.

The facilities planner can use this basic data to evaluate facilities needs in the areas described above.

Developing Cost Estimates

The information collected from the audit can be converted into estimates on an order of magnitude basis using simple replacement costs for components derived from cost publications such as *Means Square Foot Costs*.

An alternative method uses detailed estimates of labor and material costs available locally either from a maintenance staff, consultants, contractors, or material vendors. With estimates of projects completed, priorities for work assignment can be developed. (Methods of estimating using the Facilities Audit are detailed in Chapter 12.)

Users of the Data

The information gathered in the Facilities Audit will have several intended users. With this in mind, the audit manager must know who the audit is being done for and the purpose of gathering the information. Each user will desire a different level of detail for their use in facility decision-making. The systematic collection of data and progressive summaries generated by the audit can be easily extracted to form proper reports for each group. Potential users are listed and described in the following paragraphs.

Corporate Officers

The audit can provide a consistent presentation of the entire range of problems in the physical plant. It is a useful tool when setting funding priorities, especially when funding is limited. Results can also be used as documentation for capital budget requests and to help establish a facilities problem database.

Administrative Staff

Information gathered in the audit lets the administrative staff know what facilities and resources are available and confirms the condition of facilities.

Physical Plant Managers

The audit provides data for coordinating day-to-day maintenance and major project planning. The Facilities Audit helps the physical plant staff communicate with corporate officers—physical plant problems not attended to in the past could be objectively presented in the audit.

Team Specialists

The audit enables engineers, architects, and plant specialists to gather data about their particular areas. The needs of the entire team can be identified and performed objectively using the audit data. The database also simplifies overall needs to be studied.

How the Audit was Developed

In the development of this material, various audit procedures used by federal agencies, including the military services, statewide systems of higher education and individual institutions, and private corporations were examined and evaluated. An effort was made to incorporate the most effective techniques used by private consultants in the field.

The auditor systematically inspects the buildings by examining Facilities Audit components. These components are similar to the UNIFORMAT Divisions. A comparison of the Facilities Audit components and UNIFORMAT divisions is shown in Figure 8.3. The audit format in this book groups building components and procedures according to their sequential order of placement during initial construction.

A regrouping of components in the category of "Service Systems" is made to emphasize mechanical and electrical systems, as these two categories can represent 35 to 50 percent of a facility. Over the lifetime of a facility, mechanical and electrical systems account for the largest portion of maintenance and capital repairs and/or replacements. Additional categories have been added to the audit format to address safety standards. An overlapping may occur with components in other systems—stairs and exits, sprinkler systems, and electronic devices—thus special treatment of these systems is warranted in the inspection process. Finally, components addressing functional performance are added.

Means Graphic Construction Standards and *Means Facilities Maintenance Standards* are suggested references offering detailed graphic information on systems and components analyzed on the audit rating forms.

A good way to become familiar with the concept of analyzing the conditions of a building using the component method is to visualize a sample inspection. Standing outside the structure, the visible components start at the foundations, move up the exterior enclosure, including exterior surface finishes, doors, windows, and other exterior openings, and on up to the roof. The substructure and the superstructure—the structural frame—complete the Primary System. Moving into the building interior, the finished surfaces of floors, walls, ceilings, partitions, and doors comprise the Secondary Systems. The Service Systems include conveying, mechanical, and electrical systems. Experience in conducting Facilities Audits has led to a new category, Safety Standards, to evaluate life safety and building protection.

As stated earlier, some categories may overlap with components in previous items; for example, sprinklers under plumbing and stairs under superstructure. Other building components may be grouped into new configurations such as traditional, historical, aesthetic, community, and other intangible values.

Functional performance is also useful in examining some of the negative aspects of building suitability such as conflicting land use, visual and physical arrangement problems, and conflicts and attitudes detrimental to the property owner.

Audit Components and UNIFORMAT

Facilities Audit Components	UNIFORMAT
Primary Systems	
1. Foundations	1. Foundations
2. Substructure	2. Substructures
3. Superstructure	3. Superstructure
4. Exterior Closure	4. Exterior Closure
5. Roofing	5. Roofing
Secondary Systems	
6. Partitions and Doors	6. Interior Construction
7. Walls and Finishes	
8. Floor Finishes	
9. Ceiling Finishes	
Service Systems	
10. Conveying	7. Conveying
11. Mechanical: Plumbing	8. Mechanical
12. Mechanical: Heating	
13. Mechanical: Cooling	
14. Electrical: Service and Distribution	9. Electrical
15. Electrical: Lighting and Power	
Safety Standards	
16. Safety Standards	10. General Conditions
	11. Special Condition
	12. Site Work
Functional Performance	
17A. Functional Standards—Suitability and Adaptability	
17B. Functional Standards—Use Considerations	

Figure 8.3

142

Terminology

Terms used in the comprehensive Facilities Audit program are defined in the following paragraphs.

Facilities Audit

The Facilities Audit is an evaluation of the physical condition and functional performance of facilities, including buildings, grounds, utilities, and equipment.

Facilities Renewal Program

A cost effective program which integrates a regular maintenance program funded by current operating funds with:

- deferred maintenance,
- facilities remodeling and renovations,
- retrofitting for energy conservation,
- elimination of health and life safety problems, and
- provisions for handicapped accessibility.

Major Maintenance Program

Additions, repairs, remodeling, and renovations are part of the major maintenance program. Defined by scope of work and source of funding, the work is typically too complex and costly to be included in a regular maintenance program, possibly requiring funds outside of a current operating budget.

Additions

New construction attached to an existing structure as an extension is an addition. Generally, additions involve alterations within existing buildings as well.

Alterations

A change of use involving modifications to interior space is an alteration. This change is less extensive than remodeling or renovation. It includes relocation of interior space divisions; modifications to existing mechanical/electrical systems; and exterior closure.

Repairs or Remodeling

Included in this category are rebuilding or replacement in areas larger than individual spaces: partitions, ceilings, or floors; replacement of mechanical, ventilation, cooling, or electrical systems, structural components, or roofs.

Renovation or Reconstruction

This category includes conversion to new use of interior spaces requiring major demolition and rebuilding of major structural elements, mechanical/electrical systems, architectural exterior or interior treatments, internal circulation, and safety features.

Maintenance

Facilities maintenance is the upkeep of buildings, grounds, utilities, and equipment to meet assigned missions. Categories of maintenance are defined for management and budgeting purposes based on cycle of activity, scope of work, and funding allocation and sources. Four commonly used categories are listed and described below.

Emergency Maintenance: The repair or replacement of property requiring immediate attention because the functioning of a critical system is impaired, or because health, safety, security of life or property is endangered, is known as emergency maintenance. Emergency work supersedes all other categories of maintenance.

Preventive Maintenance (PM): PM involves the planned maintenance of buildings, grounds, equipment, and utilities for conditions which will lead to harmful depreciation, and any other appropriate actions to ensure continuous operation or maintenance at acceptable levels.

Planned, Routine, or Regular Maintenance: This category includes routine repairs and replacements of buildings, grounds, utilities, or equipment which are normally recurring on a more or less predictable basis. It does not involve major structural or space alterations, or major repairs.

Deferred Maintenance: Maintenance, repair and/or renewal work deferred from the normal operating budget cycle due to lack of funds are categorized as deferred maintenance.

Adapting the Audit

Careful design of a Facilities Audit enables the facilities manager to predetermine the level of detail of the information to be obtained, and to be sure the information gathered is appropriate for the projected applications of the findings. The audit system explained previously—organizing a building into components—should be followed to survey the condition of maintenance and guide immediate tasks. However, the selection of approach must be driven by the nature of an organization's facilities, budgeting methods, and organizational structure. The format for expressing the findings of the audit should be tailored to match the input requirements for the existing facility work order system.

The owner of a single property will find the audit process a valuable exercise in becoming familiar with conditions and maintenance needs. Where time and resources are limited, the facilities manager or owner may personally conduct inspections and note observations. Inevitably, there are surprises as the underestimating of priorities and costs becomes evident.

At a more sophisticated level, the facilities manager directs staff and/or consultants conducting a detailed survey. With more time and resources available, a comprehensive picture can be obtained of conditions and needs that can be evaluated and repeated in future annual audits.

Summary

The Facilities Audit process consists of three phases: (1) designing the audit; (2) collecting the data; and (3) presenting the findings. Each phase is described in detail in the following chapters.

A well-conceived audit and audit team will produce a complete and understandable statement of the condition and adequacy of facilities to perform their intended mission. The identified needs and their attendant costs can be readily evaluated by personnel at all levels in an organization in determining current and future fiscal expenditures.

Chapter Nine

PREPARING FOR THE FACILITIES AUDIT

Conducting a Facilities Audit involves a significant commitment of resources for an organization. Staff assigned must be pulled from regular tasks to inspect facilities, or manage the activities of consultants. Funds must be budgeted to cover the costs of reproducing materials, testing devices, or laboratory testing. If consultants are used, their costs must be included in the budget. Thorough preparation is necessary in coordinating these resources to produce an efficient and effective Facilities Audit. Steps in preparing for the audit are explained in this chapter.

Designing the Audit

The first phase in preparing for the Facilities Audit is the design of the audit. The steps in this phase are:

Step I. Determining the Scope of the Audit
Step II. Selecting the Audit Team

Step I involves determining those buildings, grounds, equipment, and utilities that will be covered by the audit. A decision must be made in this phase whether to conduct a comprehensive survey of all the buildings at all of an organization's locations, or to audit only a limited number of buildings. This decision is based on the primary purposes of the survey, previous surveys of conditions, available resources, and time available to produce the survey.

Next the audit team is selected—Step II. One individual should be assigned primary responsibility for the audit. Particular in-house staff are assigned to perform the survey. The use of consultants or other support staff is also determined at this time.

These steps are shown in Figure 9.1.

Determining the Scope of the Audit

Audits differ in scope, from a basic recording of observations to a complete documentation of costs and priorities for major maintenance projects. A survey may be designed for a single building type or a group of building types. However, the partial survey should eventually be integrated into a complete one. If the facility is not to be audited in its entirety at this time, select high priority facilities and components. Priorities are determined by reporting demands, age of the facility, immediate maintenance needs, emergency situations, or proposed uses.

Although the Component Rating Forms and summaries presented in this book are designed to gather and record any degree of information, some basic decisions must be made prior to beginning the audit in order to properly extend or condense the structure of the audit. These decisions are explained in the following paragraphs.

What to Include

Facilities included in the audit are determined by the purpose of the audit. Available time, personnel, and costs of consultants are other determining factors. For example, an audit may by limited to buildings only; expanded to collect information on particular building components, such as roofs; or condensed to audit only one building.

Consider the organization's overall priorities and future planning efforts. One typical distinction might be whether only **owned facilities** or **all facilities in use** are covered. Two sets of rating forms are presented in this book: Comprehensive Audit Forms for detailed building inspections (B forms, shown in the Appendix); and Condensed Audit Forms for a more general recording of inspection observations (C forms, shown at the end of this chapter). The depth of an audit is controlled initially by the selection of either the comprehensive or the condensed audit.

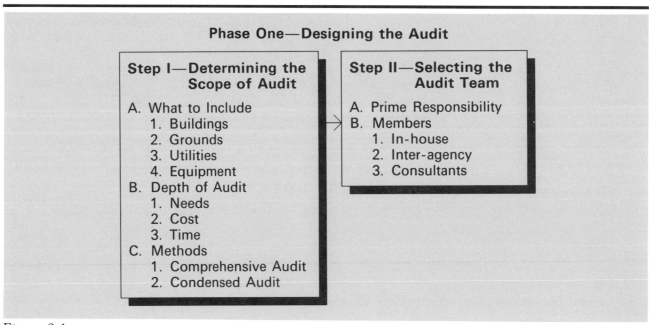

Figure 9.1

Property Information

The next choice to be made is the exact number of buildings to be included in the audit. To accomplish this task, background data on each property is organized on a Property File Form for each building, including land data. Figure 9.2 is an example of a Property File Form. Basic data from individual Property File Forms is summarized on a Building Data Summary Form (Figure 9.3), which can also be used to organize the audit program. It also serves as an index of facilities to be audited, and as a checklist on decisions for what is included in the audit. It may be preferable to list separately those facilities that are leased, under construction, vacant, to be demolished, renovated, or will undergo substantial change of use in the near future.

Depth of the Audit

A sample Component Rating Form is shown in Figure 9.4. The following opportunities on the Component Rating Forms for the comprehensive audit (shown in Appendix A) can add more detail to the audit, thereby increasing its usefulness.

Condition: An entry for one of five **condition ratings** ranging from satisfactory to unsatisfactory can be made, based on the amount of deficiencies observed by the inspector.

Cost Estimates for Maintenance: One of the major decisions that defines the scope of the audit is the use of cost estimates. If detailed cost estimates for deficiencies are desired, more information will be required at the beginning of the audit. However, when cost estimates are incorporated, the audit generates highly useful summaries outlining major maintenance costs and priorities. Including cost estimates also allows for comparisons to be made with other facilities and estimates of repair and replacement needs.

On each component rating form, there is an opportunity to enter a deficiency report, estimating the costs for correcting maintenance problems and capital projects, and total costs for correcting deficiencies.

An alternative developed by one organization noted the dimensions or quantities of a problem and entered the actual labor and material cost estimates in the comment section of the Component Rating Form.

Priorities for Maintenance: All rating forms have space for a **priority rating**, based on the results of the field inspection. Another level of priority ranking is achieved by summarizing all the major maintenance deficiencies in a building, or all the organization's buildings, in a complete inventory of priority projects.

Maintenance Deficiency Comments: Each Component Rating Form has space for an entry on **maintenance deficiency comments**. Comments on routine maintenance can be identified by category of maintenance work orders and/or maintenance projects, and transferred to work orders for remedial action. Summaries can be developed for components, groups of component assemblies, or building totals.

A.2 PROPERTY FILE

BUILDING DATA

1. Organization Name _____
2. Approved by
   Name _____ Title _____ Date _____
3. Building Number _____
4. Property Name _____
5. Property Address _____
6. Property Main Use/Special Use _____
7. Gross Area (Sq. Ft.) _____
8. Net Area (Sq. Ft.) _____
9. Type of Ownership: _____ Owned _____ Lea_____ O-L _____
10. Book Value $_____ Year Appraised _____
11. Replacement Value $_____
12. Year Constructed/Major Additions _____
13. Year Acquired _____

LAND DATA

14. Type of Ownership: _____ Owned _____ Lea _____O-L_____
15. Book Value _____ Year Appraised _____
16. Year Acquired _____
17. Size in Acres _____
18. Market Value $_____

NOTES: _____
_____
_____
_____
_____

Figure 9.2

A.1 BUILDING DATA SUMMARY

BUILDING NUMBER	BUILDING NAME	BUILDING USE*	LOCATION/ ADDRESS	OWNERSHIP** OWN/LEA/O-L

* Principal and Special Uses

** Own = Owned
   Lea = Leased
   O-L = Owned/Leased

Figure 9.3

B1.1 PRIMARY SYSTEMS – FOUNDATIONS

FAC #_____   FACILITY NAME _____   REPLACEMENT

DATE _____   INSPECTOR _____   VALUE $_____

A. SYSTEM DESCRIPTION

    (a) Footings:

        Individual Footings & Piers _____ Continuous Footings_____

        Grade Beams _____ Piles _____ Caissons _____

    (b) Foundation Wall Materials:

        Steel _____ Concrete Cast-in-place _____

        Concrete Block _____ Other _____

    (c) Waterproofing and Underdrain

        Coating _____ Membrane _____ Board _____

B. COMPONENT EVALUATION

(a) Condition Rating	(b) Deficiency Report	(c) Priority Rating
1._____	1._____	1._____
2._____	2._____	2._____
3._____	3._____	3._____
4._____	4._____	4._____
5._____	Total $ _____	

C. MAINTENANCE DEFICIENCY COMMENTS

_____

_____

_____

_____

_____

D. COMPONENT RATING: (   )   x   (   ) = _____

                              Possible   Condition   Rating

                              Rating   Value

                                         Multiplier

Figure 9.4

Selecting the Audit Team

The first step in selecting the audit team is designating the person responsible for managing the process. This person guides the process from start to finish and should be aware of the purposes, resources available, and time required to complete the audit. Coordination of information necessary to instruct inspectors and familiarity with the organization's facilities are essential skills the audit manager must possess. Building an "institutional memory" on special characteristics of facilities and maintenance problems begins with the selection of the appropriate audit manager.

Team Members

An audit team should include staff representing the three major areas of the audit: primary, secondary, and service systems. An additional person who is well-versed in safety standards may be obtained from a risk management background. Other specialists may be added as required.

A team for the medium size organization (up to 1 million gross square feet of space) or larger (more than 1 million gross square feet of space) would include:

- An audit manager responsible for coordination of the audit
- A person familiar with building construction, either an architect or building maintenance manager familiar with various trades
- A mechanical engineer or maintenance staff person from the mechanical trades
- An electrical engineer or maintenance staff person from the electrical trades
- Professional consultants or contractors as necessary for technical assistance

Use of In-house Staff

Audits are performed most successfully by in-house personnel, using outside expertise only in areas where in-house specialists are not available. Experience has shown that the best inspectors are staff maintenance personnel who work with the facilities on a routine basis, and who have access to the "collective knowledge" of operations and maintenance. Company employees are familiar with the facilities and can most accurately uncover existing problems and needs.

The training of inspectors should be directed towards understanding the process and the use of rating forms. Selected members of the audit team should possess technical knowledge of maintenance procedures and be capable of identifying problem areas and prioritizing their remedial action.

Estimating the cost of remedial work tasks uncovered in the audit can be done by staff estimators, using cost publications such as *Means Facilities Cost Data*, or prices from local contractors and vendors.

To ensure consistent results, the team should inspect the facilities as a group, even if this may hamper completion of the staff's other day-to-day responsibilities.

Outside Consultants

Outside consultants are necessary when an organization cannot use their own staff for the audit, or because special expertise is required. If consultants are used, the audit scope and format should be set up in advance by in-house staff. A representative of the facility should always coordinate the recommendations and present the findings. It is advisable to involve the staff in the audit in some manner; if special programs or efforts are to result from this audit, staff involvement and support is critical.

The request for a proposal from consultants should clearly define: the purpose of the audit; what is to be evaluated; how observations are to be recorded; how the data is to be processed; and desired reports of the results. Audit costs vary widely based on scope, recording, and reporting requirements. Be prepared to be flexible in adjusting the scope of the audit (including the budget) to fit consultant's proposals.

The audit manager, in supervising outside consultants, must monitor the process to ensure that audits conducted in future years can follow a similar format, whether performed by in-house staff or outside consultants. A one time audit which cannot be duplicated has limited benefits for long-term maintenance and capital project planning.

One advantage of contracting outside professionals to perform the audit is that the audit can be completed in a concentrated time period by people who will not be interrupted by the day-to-day requirements of plant operations and maintenance. In areas where technical expertise is necessary, the outside consultant may have access to experts whose experience often far outweighs that of the operations and maintenance staff, thus augmenting the diagnosis of the component(s) in question.

Orienting the Audit Team
The members of the audit team should have a general understanding of the audit process, along with a thorough understanding of its purpose and use.

Inspectors drawn from the operations and maintenance staff may see their assignment from a different perspective than that of the audit manager. The staff may consider the audit a nuisance, just another additional assignment, rather than seeing it as a contribution to an important organizational process. Bringing the inspectors enthusiastically into the process begins with a well-prepared orientation outlining the overall program and a thorough explanation of the rating forms. To further enthusiasm for the audit, experienced audit team members should be encouraged to offer suggestions for properly interpreting their assignments.

Key areas to be addressed in an orientation are listed and described in the following paragraphs.

Time Period: The audit team has a specific time period for collecting the data and returning the audit forms. It is particularly important that the audit forms be completed and returned promptly after completion of the inspections.

If access to a facility prevents inspectors from performing the audit on time, adjustments should be made to the schedule (see Chapter 10 for more information on scheduling).

Where there is a definite plan to repeat the audit on a timetable—annually, or less frequently—the audit team should understand the importance of conducting a thorough job.

Basic Building Data: Team members should be familiar with the rating forms and should possess basic data about each building. Data should include the following items:
- Small-scale floor plans for each building
- Construction and maintenance history
- Current use of the space
- A list of known maintenance problems

Inspection: Accompanying each rating form is an inspection checklist of anticipated problem areas (shown in the Appendix). The inspector may add other items to this list based on experience. Photographs or videotape recordings may also be used to ensure that noted deficiencies are not left off the final audit report.

During the audit, the inspector must be able to judge the priority of a problem. Priorities range from an emergency (which must be taken care of immediately to remove a life threatening or property damaging situation) to problems which can be deferred into the next annual budget cycle.

Inspectors should always see an entire set of sample completed forms before beginning the audit, even if they are only inspecting one of the components. This provides an understanding of how their contribution relates to the audit as a whole.

Detailed cost estimates for a defined need (if required) may be provided by the inspector, support staff, estimators, contractors, or vendors.

Reports: A variety of reports can be produced from the audit. The team members should be familiar with these reports to fully understand the purpose of the assignment.

Management Actions: The team should be briefed on any management actions to be taken as a result of the audit. Primary actions resulting from the audit are work orders or capital projects for:

- Emergency maintenance
- Preventive maintenance
- Planned, routine, or regular maintenance
- Deferred maintenance

Actual schedules for these tasks will be produced from the final analyses of priorities and available resources.

Summary

In conclusion, it is important to design a suitable audit well before the audit process begins. This includes determining the scope of the audit—deciding whether to audit every building or choosing to audit only certain buildings or building components. The audit team must also be carefully selected. Specific persons are assigned specific areas of responsibility.

It is advisable to review the design section of this chapter before starting data collection; it is easier to adapt the self-evaluation process to a specific facility before beginning the inspection period.

Chapter Ten

▌CONDUCTING A FACILITIES AUDIT

Accurate and timely collection of data is perhaps the most critical element in producing a realistic assessment of a facility's condition. The facilities manager must produce a schedule incorporating all items to be audited. Forms must be designed that will accurately record deficiencies of a particular facility. Data is then collected on Component Rating Forms. Finally, this data must be summarized for evaluation and analysis.

The data collection phase has three steps: Step I—Designing a plan of attack, Step II—Collecting the data, and Step III—Evaluating and analyzing the data. These steps are illustrated in Figure 10.1 and explained in this chapter.

Designing a Plan of Attack

In this step, the Facilities Audit is organized for inspecting and rating a specific facility. A set of Component Rating Forms and checklists is prepared for each building to be audited, using the forms shown in the Appendix as a guide, and a schedule is produced. The checklist shown in Figure 10.2 lists the important elements to be finalized during this stage.

Scheduling

An audit schedule is produced, before beginning to collect data. The Building Data Summary (see Chapter 9, Figure 9.3) can be used as a checklist to ensure that all buildings to be inspected are included on the schedule.

All aspects of the overall process—inspections, processing the data, and preparing reports for management—should be scheduled. Sometimes, if there has never been a previous audit, or if there are delays in finding the "right" time to perform the audit, a schedule may be imposed by senior management. Although initiative for an audit should come directly from the facilities management staff, with the findings reviewed by senior management, such an imposed schedule may actually be a "mixed blessing."

The time it takes to complete a Facilities Audit depends on the number of buildings, priorities set for inspections, availability of audit staff, and data evaluation resources.

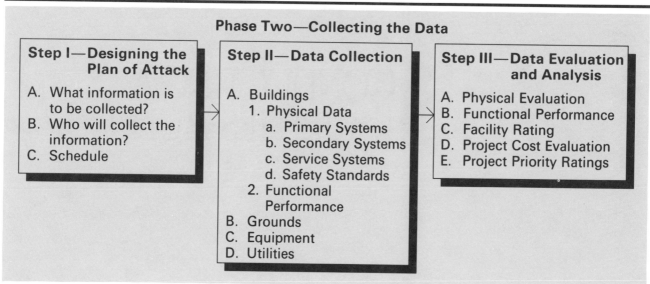

Figure 10.1

Checklist for Designing the Plan of Attack

1. Master Schedule: Use the Building Evaluation Summary to outline the buildings to be surveyed (See Chapter 9, Figure 9.3).

2. Finalize whether the Comprehensive Audit Forms or the Condensed Audit Forms are to be used for rating the facilities. (A full set of audit forms is shown in the Appendix).

3. Finalize the choices of audit team leader and team members.

4. Confirm whether cost estimates are to be included for maintenance deficiencies and select an estimating method.

5. Be sure that the Building Evaluation Summary and Component Rating Forms contain replacement values and possible ratings, and are ready for distribution to team members.

6. Establish a time schedule for each building audit.

7. Be sure that team members have been briefed with an orientation and that small scale drawings, building histories, and building access are available. This is the time to make sure that audit procedures are thoroughly understood by all team members.

Figure 10.2

In scheduling the audit, consider any locations with special needs. Special needs should be identified and any changes made in the audit schedule.

Figure 10.3 is a sample audit schedule.

Data Collection

In the data collection step, the inspectors fill out the Building Evaluation Summary, the sixteen Component Rating Forms, and the two Functional Performance Forms. Assistance from an estimating source—staff or consultants—may be necessary if estimates are to be included on the forms.

Physical Data

The inspection begins with a physical analysis of the building. The physical analysis is recorded on the Component Rating Forms (shown in the Appendix). The analysis is done by grouping building assemblies into four categories: the Primary System, Secondary Systems, Service Systems, and Safety Standards. These categories are described in the following paragraphs.

Primary System: The primary system includes the load-bearing elements of a building and the exterior enclosure. The primary system is comprised of footings, foundations, structural frame, roofing, exterior walls and finishes, insulation, doors, and windows.

Secondary Systems: This system includes architectural elements and items normally appearing in room and door finish schedules: floors, walls, ceilings, interior doors, and windows.

Service Systems: Conveying systems and all mechanical and electrical components are included in this category: elevators, escalators, lifts, plumbing, heating, cooling, ventilation, electrical service and distribution, lighting, and power.

Safety Standards: All items necessary to achieve life safety and fire protection are categorized as safety standards.

Adaptability of the Forms

Individual project conditions vary so widely on groundwork, site work, equipment, and utilities, that individualized forms should be created by the audit team to meet specific needs. For example, equipment might be included as a building component. In this case, a form for equipment would be added to the component forms.

	Sample Audit Schedule									
Week	1	2	3	4	5	6	7	8	9	10
Phase 1	x --- x --- x									
Phase 2			x --- x --- x --- x --- x							
Phase 3							x --- x --- x --- x			

Note: Do not forget to build in any time dependent on outside or uncontrollable activities, such as routine operational cycles of business, facility availability, staff time conflicts or availability of key staff members or support staff, etc.

Figure 10.3

In addition, the rating terms may be modified to meet the needs of individual facilities. For example, definitions for the Condition Rating category have undergone changes by some organizations after experience with the rating forms. One university changed the rating scale from 5 to 10 categories to provide a better range of choices for rating conditions. The definitions can and should be changed as necessary to facilitate ease of rating.

Filling Out the Rating Forms

The component rating forms are given to the inspector(s) by the team manager. The team manager should clearly explain the possible ratings to be entered on each form. Familiarization with the rating terms will enable the inspectors to make quick observations and to enter them on the rating forms.

An inspection checklist with typical deficiencies for each component is included on the page facing each Component Rating Form (a complete set of forms is shown in the Appendix). Inspectors should be encouraged to add items to the checklists based on their experience.

Steps in completing the Component Rating Forms for a building inspection are summarized in Figure 10.4 and explained below.

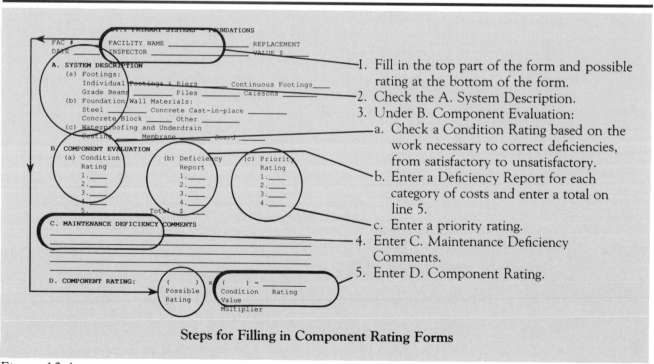

1. Fill in the top part of the form and possible rating at the bottom of the form.
2. Check the A. System Description.
3. Under B. Component Evaluation:
   a. Check a Condition Rating based on the work necessary to correct deficiencies, from satisfactory to unsatisfactory.
   b. Enter a Deficiency Report for each category of costs and enter a total on line 5.
   c. Enter a priority rating.
4. Enter C. Maintenance Deficiency Comments.
5. Enter D. Component Rating.

Steps for Filling in Component Rating Forms

Figure 10.4

Audit Team Manager Responsibility

The audit team manager fills out the Building Evaluation Summary. Data on the facility number and name, date of construction, building area, original cost, and replacement cost can be obtained from the Property File Form (Figure 9.2, Chapter 9). Replacement costs can be developed from insurance data or by estimating the costs for a similar facility described in *Means Facilities Cost Data*, indexed by location.

The possible rating can also be developed using data from a similar facility, recent construction costs, or published sources such as *Means Square Foot Costs*. The possible ratings shown on the Building Evaluation Summary in Figure 10.5 show the value of components for a one to four story office building. The cost of each component was calculated based on a percentage of the total construction costs using the 1989 edition of *Means Square Foot Costs*.

Values entered as possible ratings can be adjusted for each component for a total of 100. An organization may have compiled data on their own cost percentages or other local experience which can be used for each component.

Each Component Rating Form has four sections to be completed by the inspector. These sections are described in the following paragraphs.

Inspector Responsibility

A. System Description

The sample system description has entries to be checked for:

(a) Footings
(b) Foundation Walls and Materials
(c) Waterproofing and Underdrains

The number of entries in the system description can be tailored for special building types or to add elements, such as special equipment. The possible ratings for each component should be changed on the Building Evaluation Summary if there are any revisions to the system descriptions.

Figure 10.6 is a sample system description, as the inspector would receive it—already filled out by the audit manager.

B. Component Evaluation

Each Component Rating Form contains a section labelled B. Component Evaluation. The inspector enters an evaluation of the conditions for a building component in this section, in three different columns: the condition rating; the deficiency report; and the priority rating. Figure 10.7 shows this section of the form as it would be filled out by an inspector.

If the inspection is limited to specific components sections, they should have been identified in advance during the audit design.

Each column of the B. Component Evaluation section on the Component Rating Forms is described below.

(a) Condition Ratings: The left hand column, (a) Condition Rating, allows inspectors to rate component conditions in five categories ranging from **satisfactory** to **unsatisfactory**. The classification scheme used follows a system developed by the National Center for Educational Statistics for a survey of higher education facilities—the Higher Education Facilities Inventory and Classification Survey.

B 1 BUILDING EVALUATION SUMMARY

I.   BUILDING INFORMATION

FAC#_____FACILITY NAME_____LOCATION_____
DATE_____INSPECTOR_____
YEAR CONSTR,ADDN_____
GROSS SQ FT_____NET SQ FT_____
ORIGINAL COST $_____REPLACEMENT COST $_____

II. COMPONENT RATING

COMPONENT	RATING	
	Possible*	Actual
Primary Systems	**[35]**	
1. Foundations	3	_____
2. Substructure	2	_____
3. Superstructure	16	_____
4. Exterior Closure	12	_____
5. Roofing	2	_____
Secondary Systems	**[15]**	
6. Partitions and Doors	6	_____
7. Walls & Finishes	3	_____
8. Floors & Finishes	3	_____
9. Ceilings & Finishes	3	_____
Service Systems	**[38]**	
10. Conveying	4	_____
11. Mechanical:Plumbing	7	_____
12. Mechanical:Heating	12	_____
13. Mechanical:Cooling & Ventilation	7	_____
14. Electrical:Service & Distribution	4	_____
15. Electrical:Lighting & Power	4	_____
Safety Standards	**[4]**	
16. Safety Standards	4	_____
Functional Standards	**[8]**	
17A. Suitability & Adaptability	4	_____
17B. Use Considerations	4	_____

III. BUILDING RATING SUMMARY

Building Rating_____   [100]   (_____)

*Note: Possible Ratings vary for every building

Figure 10.5

B 1.1 PRIMARY SYSTEMS - FOUNDATIONS

FAC #_____   FACILITY NAME_____REPLACEMENT

DATE_____   INSPECTOR_____VALUE $_____

A. SYSTEM DESCRIPTION

    (a) Footings:
        Individual Footings & Piers_____ Continuous Footings__✓__
        Grade Beams_____   Piles_____   Caissons_____
    (b) Foundation Wall Materials:
        Steel _____ Concrete Cast-in-place __✓__
        Concrete Block _____ Other _____
    (c) Waterproofing and Underdrain
        Coating _____ Membrane _____ Board __✓__

B. COMPONENT EVALUTION

(a) Condition Rating	(b) Deficiency Report	(c) Priority Rating
1._____	1._____	1._____
2._____	2._____	2._____
3._____	3._____	3._____
4._____	4._____	4._____
5._____	Total $ _____	

C. MAINTENANCE DEFICIENCY COMMENTS

_____
_____
_____
_____
_____

D. COMPONENT RATING: (_____) x (_____) = _____
                  Possible   Condition   Rating
                  Rating   Value
                                Multiplier

Figure 10.6

B 1.1 PRIMARY SYSTEMS – FOUNDATIONS

FAC #_____   FACILITY NAME_____REPLACEMENT

DATE_____   INSPECTOR_____VALUE $_____

A. SYSTEM DESCRIPTION

    (a) Footings:
    Individual Footings & Piers_____ Continuous Footings_____
    Grade Beams_____ Piles_____ Caissons_____
    (b) Foundation Wall Materials:
    Steel _____ Concrete Cast-in-place _____
    Concrete Block _____ Other _____
    (c) Waterproofing and Underdrain
    Coating _____ Membrane _____ Board _____

B. COMPONENT EVALUTION

(a) Condition Rating	(b) Deficiency Report	(c) Priority Rating
1._____	1._____	1._____
2._✓_____	2._____	2._____
3._____	3._____	3._____
4._____	4._____	4._____
5._____	Total $ _____	

C. MAINTENANCE DEFICIENCY COMMENTS

_____
_____
_____
_____
_____

D. COMPONENT RATING: (   ) x (   ) = _____
                Possible   Condition   Rating
                Rating   Value
                           Multiplier

Figure 10.7

An entry is made by the inspector on *one* of the five lines indicating the average condition of the items listed under the system description. The judgment is based on selecting one of the following ratings after thoroughly considering the weighting of overall observations.

1. Satisfactory: Suitable for continued use with normal maintenance. No capital funds are needed for the next five years.
2. Remodeling A: Building conditions are currently adequate. This type of building requires restoration to present acceptable standards without major room use changes, alterations, or modernizations. The approximate cost of a Remodeling A building is not greater than 25% of the component's estimated replacement cost.
3. Remodeling B: A building in this category is in need of major updating and/or modernization. The approximate cost of a Remodeling B building is greater than 25%, but not greater than 50%, of the component's estimated replacement cost.
4. Remodeling C: Major remodeling is necessary to ensure the physical adequacy of this type of building. The approximate cost of Remodeling C is greater than 50% of the component's estimated replacement cost.
5. Unsatisfactory: Despite space needs or availability of funds for replacement, unsatisfactory buildings should be demolished or abandoned because they are unsafe or structurally unsound.

Objectivity and consistency in judging the condition rating should be impressed upon the inspectors.

Inspectors must be able to determine the approximate cost of remodeling in order to use the ratings detailed above. One method to assess the deficiency repair costs of each component uses **replacement values**. These values are calculated for the total facility and the components being inspected. For example, a building has a replacement value of $1,000,000 and foundations have a cost equal to 3% of the total replacement value. This percentage can be developed using prices from cost references such as *Means Facilities Cost Data*, or an organization's construction cost history. A calculation of 3% of the total replacement value equals $30,000. The percentage of the total replacement for this component is equivalent to the possible rating of 3 of a possible total of 100.

Assuming that $5,000 was estimated to correct foundation deficiencies, a ratio of repair costs to replacement value is used to find the percent of deficiencies.

$$\frac{\text{Repair Costs}}{\text{Component Replacement Value}} \times 100 = \underline{\hspace{1cm}}\%,$$

$$\frac{\$\ 5,000}{\$30,000} \times 100 = 16\%, \text{ then}$$

Percent of Deficiencies = 16%

The result of the example, 16%, falls into the Remodeling A category, therefore, line # 2 under (a) Condition Rating is checked.

At this point, the audit may be complete without providing cost estimates or rating priorities. However, creating estimates during the building audit is often an important objective of the audit. Adding the cost estimate to the audit increases the kinds of summary reports available and expands its usefulness. For these reasons, it is recommended that the method shown here be followed as the next step in the audit process.

(b) *Deficiency Reports*: The middle column under B. Component Evaluation, (b) Deficiency Reports, can be used to introduce estimates for remedial action to correct problems. This is an optional feature of the audit process which allows an inspector's observations and estimate to be recorded directly on the rating form. The terms and suggested cost ranges can be modified to fit an organization's work order and budgeting practices. This entry is the summary of the items listed in the third section of the form—C. Maintenance Deficiency Comments. If there are several categories of cost ranges, the total is entered under (b) Deficiency Report, and each category is individually detailed under C. Maintenance Deficiency Comments.

Costs are estimated either in the field by inspectors or provided by staff support, consultants, contractors, or vendors. The field inspector should retain notes of observed conditions and estimating calculations with suggested methods of repair, labor, and materials. The following terms can be used to estimate the suggested cost ranges of repairs. (These terms and cost ranges can be modified to conform to an organization's work task definitions and capital budget practices.)

1. No Work		$ 0
2. Maintenance Work Order	less than	$ 1,000
3. Maintenance Project(s)	between	$ 1,000–$50,000
4. Capital Project(s)	more than	$50,000
Total		$_____

If item 1. is checked off, this indicates that "No Work" (or expense) is required. If an entry is made for "No Work", the following items are left blank.

If item 2. is filled in, a "Maintenance Work Order" is designated, meaning deficiencies are estimated to cost less than $1,000 and can be prepared as a routine work order for task assignment. The total for all maintenance work orders is placed on this line.

If item 3. is filled in, a "Maintenance Project" is designated. An estimated cost range should be written on this line. Staff assistance may be required (to produce the estimate) before the inspector completes this entry on the form. The total for all maintenance projects for the component is placed on this line.

If item 4. is filled in, a "Capital Project" is designated. This indicates that repair costs exceed $50,000. The inspector usually requires technical assistance in the preparation of this type of estimate. The total for all capital projects for the component being inspected is placed on this line.

The bottom line, "Total $," is the total cost of all deficiency reports for the given component.

(Note: The $50,000 limit on items (3) and (4) can be adjusted to conform to an organization's practices for capitalizing repairs and renovations.)

An alternative to make use of labor and material actual estimates is the **replacement method**. In this method, the actual rating given a component is based on the judgment of the inspector. Compared to the possible rating, this represents the difference between the replacement cost of a component and the costs to remedy the deficiency. The Building Evaluation Summary Form provides the possible rating for each component, assigned as a percentage of the total replacement value of the building. The steps for using this method are listed below:

1. A building replacement value is determined and entered on the Building Evaluation Summary.
2. A replacement value for each component is calculated and entered at the top of each component form.
3. The component rating at the bottom of each form is subtracted from the possible rating and multiplied by the component replacement cost to find the cost of correcting the deficiencies. This amount can be entered on line # 1 under (b) Deficiency Report in the B. Component Evaluation section of the form.

For example, a building with a total replacement value of $1,000,000 has a component with a replacement cost of $30,000. This is equal to a possible rating of 3. If the actual rating is 2, the "deficit" is the difference between the possible and actual ratings. In this case 1 (3-2), or 1%, is multiplied by $1,000,000 to arrive at the cost of correcting the deficiency:

$$\$1,000,000 \times .01 = \$10,000$$

(c) *Priority Rating*: The right hand column under B. Component Evaluation, (c) Priority Rating, is the inspector's judgment of the priority of an observed deficiency. This section of the rating form provides guidance for facilities managers to review overall deficiencies. It is a valuable tool for developing maintenance schedules and capital budgets.

The inspector should be familiar with the following priority rating terms, commonly used in maintenance management.

1. Emergency: This designation indicates work demanding immediate attention to repair an essential operating system or building component, or because life safety or property is endangered. A response should occur within two hours of notification.
2. Urgent: Work demanding prompt attention to alleviate temporary emergency repairs or a condition requiring correction within one to five days to prevent a subsequent emergency is classified as urgent.
3. Routine: A specific completion date can be requested or required for routine work. This includes work that has no short range effect on life safety, security of personnel, or property. Routine work can be planned in detail and incorporated into a trade backlog for scheduling within twelve months.
4. Deferred: Projects that can be deferred into the following year's work planning are classified as deferred.

C. Maintenance Deficiency Comments

Cost estimates for deficiencies noted in the categories of maintenance work order, maintenance projects, and capital projects, are detailed in this space. Totals for each of these items, if any, are entered in the appropriate line under (b) Deficiency Reports (above). Figure 10.8 is a sample component form, showing typical maintenance deficiency comments.

D. Component Rating

To determine the actual Component Rating, the possible rating for the component (from the Building Evaluation Summary, Figure 10.5) is multiplied by a **Condition Value Multiplier**. The Condition Value Multiplier is calculated from the line checked by the inspector under B. Component Evaluation, (a) Condition Rating.

The steps for determining the Component Rating are listed below.

1. *Possible Rating*: Select the possible rating from the Building Evaluation Summary (Figure 10.5) for the component and enter this rating in the parentheses above "possible rating."

B 1.1 PRIMARY SYSTEMS - FOUNDATIONS

FAC #_____   FACILITY NAME_____REPLACEMENT

DATE_____   INSPECTOR_____VALUE $_____

A. SYSTEM DESCRIPTION

    (a) Footings:
       Individual Footings & Piers_____ Continuous Footings_____
       Grade Beams_____   Piles_____   Caissons_____
    (b) Foundation Wall Materials:
       Steel _____ Concrete Cast-in-place _____
       Concrete Block _____ Other _____
    (c) Waterproofing and Underdrain
       Coating _____ Membrane _____ Board _____

B. COMPONENT EVALUTION

(a) Condition Rating	(b) Deficiency Report	(c) Priority Rating
1._____	1._____	1._____
2._____	2._____	2._____
3._____	3. ✓	3._____
4._____	4._____	4._____
5._____	Total $ _____	

C. MAINTENANCE DEFICIENCY COMMENTS

Cracks from settling. Estimated at $10,000.
Moisture on inside northeast corner of
foundation wall

D. COMPONENT RATING: (   ) x (   ) = _____
                Possible   Condition   Rating
                Rating   Value
                          Multiplier

Figure 10.8

2. *Condition Value Multiplier*: Values from the (a) Condition Rating column are converted to a multiplier on a scale of 0.0 to 1.0 based on the ease or difficulty of correcting the component deficiency. For example, if line # 3 was checked by the inspector, the range of choice for the multiplier is 0.4 to 0.6. (See Figure 10.9 for suggested condition value multipliers for each condition rating.)

3. *Rating*: The possible rating (from the possible ratings column of the Building Evaluation Summary) is multiplied by the Condition Value Multiplier and the product is entered on the line above Rating and transferred to the Building Evaluation Summary (Figure 10.8) under the actual ratings column.

For example, the Primary System (the foundation) of a building has a condition report rating of 2, and the Condition Value Multiplier selected is 0.8. The possible rating for this example for a four story office building's foundations is 3; the possible rating (3) is multiplied by the Condition Value Multiplier of 0.8 to obtain the component rating:

$$3 \times 0.8 = 2.4$$

Functional Performance

Prior to determining the final rating for a building, the use and value, or functional performance, of the facility should be considered. For example, in the physical evaluation, a building may be classified in the Unsatisfactory, or demolition, category. However, for historic, aesthetic reasons or other policies, a facility may be retained for remodeling and extended use. On the other hand, a facility may fall into the remodeling categories, but the organization may want to recommend demolition because of conflicts with other plans for future land use.

The functional performance evaluation should be performed by someone with a comprehensive knowledge of the present use and total space inventory of the organization. To determine the functional performance of a building, examine the suitability of use for its present occupancy, as well as for potential future uses. Assignable space and adaptability or suitability for present and future uses should also be studied.

Condition	(a) Condition Rating	Condition Value Multiplier	
1. Satisfactory	1 _____	1.0	< 5%
			< 11%
2. Remodeling A	2 _____	0.8 ± .1	< 18%
			< 25%
3. Remodeling B	3 _____	0.5 ± .1	< 41%
			< 60%
4. Remodeling C	4 _____	0.2 ± .1	< 70%
			< 80%
5. Unsatisfactory	5 _____	0.0	> 80%

Condition Value Multipliers for Condition Ratings

Figure 10.9

Functional performance is reported on two forms. Together, these forms evaluate the suitability of a building for its present use and provide an invaluable reference for studies of future uses. The assignability of space is analyzed for future use, and various qualitative conditions such as traditional, historic, aesthetic, community, and other intangible values. Functional performance is also useful in examining some of the negative aspects of facility suitability, such as conflicting land use, visual and physical arrangement problems, conflicts, and attitudes detrimental to the organization in future planning. The Functional Standards Forms are illustrated in Figures 10.10 and 10.11.

Condensed Facilities Audit

The condensed audit shifts the emphasis of the audit from determining an overall facility evaluation of ratings for comparative purposes to an analysis of component conditions for deficiencies.

A Condensed Facilities Audit is appropriate for an organization that has already conducted a Comprehensive Facilities Audit and merely wants to update the data. Lack of resources to allocate staff, costs, or deadlines may also dictate a shorter audit process. In some cases, the evaluation of component parts of a structure and an overall building summary may require time and resources that are inappropriate to an organization's size and type of facilities.

This "shortcut" procedure should be thoroughly considered before accepting it as a substitute for a comprehensive audit. Carefully review the background material and content of this chapter before selecting the condensed audit approach.

Four forms (shown in Figures 10.12 through 10.15) are suggested for use in the condensed audit: a Building Data Summary Form; a Building Condition Analysis Form; a Project Request for Repair and Renovation Form; and a Five Year Repair and Renovation Form. These forms compile a minimum level of information about a facility and its maintenance and capital project needs.

The Condensed Audit Forms should be prepared by someone who is familiar with the facility and the organization's overall space. This person may be a permanent member of the audit team or may be assigned from elsewhere in the organization because of their special knowledge.

Data Evaluation and Analysis

In the final step of the data collection phase, the inspection forms are collected by the team manager, verified for completion, and a Building Evaluation Summary filled out. If deficiency reports were entered on the component forms, these are summarized to identify categories of work tasks, cost estimates, maintenance orders, maintenance projects, and capital projects. Also, if priority ratings were created for the deficiency reports, they should be included on the summary.

Building Evaluation Summary

The summary should be filled out by the audit team leader, to complete his or her responsibilities in the data collection phase. The Building Evaluation Summary (Figure 10.5) serves as a review of the work done by inspectors, to ensure that all components were inspected, while compiling a summary for each audited building.

The top part of the summary form has a space for Building Information, that should have been completed by the team manager prior to the inspection.

B1.17A FUNCTIONAL STANDARDS – SUITABILITY & ADAPTABILITY

FAC #_____   FACILITY NAME _____

DATE _____   INSPECTOR _____

A. SYSTEM DESCRIPTION
- (a) Flexible Design Concept _____
- (b) Partitions (Demountable or Rigid) _____
- (c) Specialized Building Type _____
- (d) Flexible Service Systems _____
- (e) Stationary Equipment _____
- (f) Functional Spaces _____
- (g) Working Environment _____
- (h) Circulation and Functional Relationships _____
- (i) Conflicting Uses _____
- (j) Code Conformance _____
- (k) Deferred Maintenance _____

B. COMPONENT EVALUTION
- (a) Condition Rating
    - 1._____
    - 2._____
    - 3._____
    - 4._____
    - 5._____

C. COMMENTS:

_____
_____
_____
_____
_____
_____

D. COMPONENT RATING: (   )   x   (   )   =   _____

       Possible   Condition   Rating
       Rating   Value
                 Multiplier

Figure 10.10

B1.17B FUNCTIONAL STANDARDS – USE CONSIDERATIONS

FAC #_____   FACILITY NAME_____
DATE_____   INSPECTOR_____

A. SYSTEM DESCRIPTION

1. **Traditional Values**   Significant role or meaning relative to organization's customs, traditional practices or values.

2. **Historic Values**   Significance to the organization or community for historic associations similar to National Register of Historic places criteria.

3. **Esthetic Value**   Visual qualities and physical relationships with other buildings or the landscape.

4. **Social/Community Values** Benefits or detriments to location and/or community.

5. **Interim Use**   Facility can be used temporarily for other uses.

6. **Future Land Use**   Conflicting land use with future plans.

7. **Suitability**   Spatial characteristics relative to specific use or is suitable for highly specialized use difficult to replace.

8. **Intangible Values**   Orientation, psychological environment, noise, odors, etc.

B. COMPONENT EVALUATION

(a) Condition Rating

    1._____
    2._____
    3._____
    4._____
    5._____

C. COMMENTS:

_____
_____
_____
_____
_____

D. COMPONENT RATING: (   )   x   (   )   =   _____
                              Possible   Condition   Rating
                              Rating   Value
                                                Multiplier

Figure 10.11

C.1 BUILDING DATA SUMMARY

BUILDING NUMBER	BUILDING NAME	BUILDING USE*	LOCATION/ ADDRESS	OWNERSHIP** OWN/LEA/O-L

*Principal and Special Uses

** Own = Owned
   Lea = Leased
   O-L = Owned/Leased

Figure 10.12

C.2 BUILDING CONDITION ANALYSIS

1. BUILDING INFORMATION

Bldg _____   Bldg Name _____   Location _____

Date _____   Inspector _____

Year Const, Addn _____

Gross Sq Ft _____   Net Sq Ft _____

2. BUILDING CONDITION ANALYSIS

Building Component	Condition	Repair/Renovation Recommendation
A. Primary Structure		
1. Foundations		
2. Substructure		
3. Superstructure		
4. Exterior Closure		
5. Roofing		
B. Secondary Structure		
6. Partitions & Doors		
7. Walls & Finishes		
8. Floor Finishes		
9. Ceiling Finishes		
C. Service Systems		
10. Conveying		
11. Mechanical: Plumbing		
12. Mechanical: Heating & Ventilating		
13. Mechancial: Cooling		
14. Electrical: Service & Distribution		
15. Electrical: Lighting & Power		
D. Safety Standards		
16. Egress		
17. Fire Ratings		
18. Extinguishing Systems		
19. Detection & Alarms		
20. Emergency Power		
E. Energy Conservation		
21. Source of Energy		
22. HVAC		
23. Lighting		
24. Insulation		
F. Handicapped Access		
25. Circulation		
26. Services		
G. Functional Standards		
27. Adaptability		
28. Use Considerations		

Figure 10.13

C.3 PROJECT REQUEST FOR REPAIR AND RENOVATION

_____ _____FY

 Location

_____

 Building

1. Project Title _____

2. Priority Number _____

3. Project Description and Justification _____
_____
_____
_____
_____
_____
_____
_____
_____
_____

4. Project Cost Estimate
   Labor $_____
   Materials $_____
   Design Fee $_____
   Owner's Cost $_____
   Contingency $_____

5. Project Schedule

_____

Start Design   Bid   Const Start   Complete

6. Estimate Prepared By: _____

Figure 10.14

C.4 FIVE YEAR REPAIR AND RENOVATION PROGRAM

Priority Number	Fiscal Year	Project Description	Estimated Cost

Figure 10.15

The second part of the form, the Component Rating Summary, lists the components inspected. This can also serve as a checklist for the team manager in reviewing the completeness of the Facilities Audit. For this portion of the form, a possible rating is entered in the corresponding column. This rating may be derived from publications such as *Means Square Foot Cost Data* for similar building types.

Possible ratings have been filled in on Figure 10.8 for a four story office building of 60,000 square feet.

The actual rating is taken from the last part of the Component Rating Forms, as explained in the previous section. The building rating is the total of the actual ratings for all building components.

Summary

After reviewing the audit inspection procedures, the audit team is ready to begin the building analysis. Component Rating Forms are filled out as explained in this chapter. Next, components of each building are summarized on the Building Evaluation Summary, ready for analysis and presentation of findings.

A complete set of Facilities Audit Forms is included in the Appendix: the Building Data Forms, the Component Rating Forms, the Functional Standards Forms, the Condensed Audit Forms, and the Building Evaluation Summary.

Chapter Eleven

CONCLUDING THE FACILITIES AUDIT

The third phase of the self-evaluation process is summarizing the findings of the Facilities Audit. The three steps in this phase are:
Step I—Summarizing, Step II—Setting Priorities, and Step III—Reporting/Presenting. These steps are illustrated in Figure 11.1.

Summarizing the Audit

Audit summaries may be organized in several different ways: by all facilities audited or individual facilities; by all building systems or individual building systems; and by all building components or individual building components.

Deficiency reports and priority ratings, if collected by the inspectors, may be presented in the summary reports. For example, maintenance work orders, maintenance projects, or capital projects and projects by building type or component types can be organized separately. If an Energy Audit is also conducted, the summary could list and evaluate energy conservation projects.

The summary should be more than facts and figures. A narrative should describe the audit process and draw conclusions on overall facility conditions, adequacy of current funding for maintenance, and capital projects.

Report Listings

In the Comprehensive Audit, the Building Evaluation Summary (Figure 10.5) and Component Rating Forms (See Appendix) provide the data for summary reports. Condensed Audit Forms (Figures 10.12 through 10.15) provide information for summaries of the Condensed Audit. A suggested list of reports is presented below.

All Facilities

1. Report # 1—Facilities Audit Building Ratings
2. Report # 2—Summary Data for a Building System
3. Report # 3—Summary Data for a Building Component
4. Report # 4—Maintenance Work Order Summary (< $1,000)
5. Report # 5—Maintenance Project Summary ($1,000–$50,000)
6. Report # 6—Capital Project Summary (> $50,000)
7. Report # 7—Total Maintenance Deficiency Cost Estimates
8. Report # 8—Building Data Summaries (Building Area, Replacement Value, Building Age, etc.)
9. Report # 9—Facilities Audit Schedule

Individual Facilities

10. Report # 10—Maintenance Work Orders (< $1,000)
11. Report # 11—Maintenance Projects ($1,000—$50,000)
12. Report # 12—Capital Projects (> $50,000)
13. Report # 13—Total Maintenance Deficiency Cost Estimates
14. Report # 14—Component Summaries by Priority (Roofing, Painting, Plumbing, Alarm Systems, etc.)
15. Report # 15—Functional Standards Summary

Deferred maintenance problems are often the incentive for starting the audit process. A thoroughly prepared and summarized Facilities Audit will provide the basis for evaluating deferred maintenance and costs required for remedying deteriorating conditions.

Besides the deferred maintenance question, the functional performance evaluation allows two critical questions to be addressed: *Is the facility suitable for its current use, or will it require remodeling? What is the total cost compared to a new building and is relocation to another building feasible or desirable?*

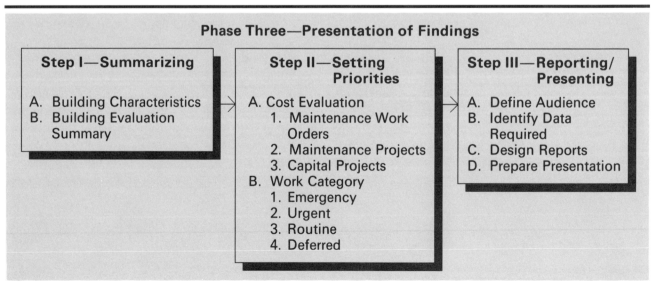

Figure 11.1

Comments from the audit are also helpful in producing feasibility studies of renovations or changes in building use.

Computer Applications

The audit method described in this book was designed for manual use but is readily adaptable to computer applications. Careful analysis of the desired forms and information to be obtained from the audit is required before designing individual screens for each form and report. This can be achieved on word processing and spreadsheet software for generating forms for use by inspectors. More sophisticated programming allows faster preparation of summaries where there is a computing capability available to handle the data from a Facilities Audit.

Cost estimates can be easily updated for inflation or modified for changing conditions if data is stored in computer generated form and maintenance and capital project calculations are programmed.

Setting Priorities

The Facilities Audit will furnish two types of information to senior administrators and other decision-makers who need to set facilities priorities. First, those facilities that have the greatest need based on the severity of both physical conditions and functional performance can be selected; second, the audit results will help plan maintenance tasks and capital project budgeting.

Priority selections from the Facilities Audit can be made for several purposes. Maintenance work orders, maintenance projects, and capital projects can be estimated and scheduled for work assignment. Management priority decisions on operating and capital budgets are supported by the Facilities Audit information.

Maintenance Deficiency Estimates

Maintenance deficiency comments entered on the Component Rating Forms can be estimated, preferably using quantities of labor and materials, design fees, and other owner's costs. General estimates of costs from similar projects are not specific enough to determine priorities. Reliable sources should be used.

Where staff is available, their experience with maintenance and similar projects is vital for estimating projects. Architects, contractors, vendors, and special consultants should be retained for assistance in preparing estimates where necessary.

Priorities by Character of Work

Categorization of priorities requires consistent treatment of deficiencies noted in the audit and functional improvement requests, since funding decisions are made based on these categories. Typically, categorizing involves separating capital projects from maintenance work orders or maintenance projects, estimating project requests, and then summarizing project requests for a five-year budgeting cycle. Funding priorities are based on a systematic categorization, developing a plan for funding maintenance and capital projects from operating budgets or special funding allocations for capital projects.

A comparison of building ratings will not automatically show the order in which items should be addressed. For example, a facility that rates a 74 is not automatically worse than one that rates a 75. However, it is valid to conclude that those facilities in the 50-74 range will need more immediate attention than those in the 75-100 range. Also, each location has its own priorities—the audit results may not show some qualitative elements that would affect funding.

One suggested outline for ranking priorities by point values is shown in Figure 11.2. Three priority levels are described which can be interpreted from the Component Rating Forms and maintenance deficiency comments. The audit team manager adds his or her knowledge of overall plant conditions. Careful judgment is necessary in choosing the priorities to fit with strategic planning and other policy considerations.

Another scheme of selecting priorities using broad descriptive categories are grouped to assist in determining priorities. Suggested categories are listed and described below.

1. *Liability Proposals*: Special matters requiring early attention to remove jeopardy through life safety, property damage, regulatory, or court ordered actions which represent liability proposals.

2. *Program and Operational Purposes*: Actions necessary to support an organization's mission and meet operational requirements are grouped under this category.

3. *Economy and Efficiency Measures*: Projects which also support program and operational objectives, but deserve special attention because they will result in immediate or eventual cost savings, are categorized as economy and efficiency measures.

Separate Priority Lists

Separate priority lists can be developed from the deficiency reports entered on the Component Rating Forms to fit budgeting practices of the operations and maintenance department and decisions by the facility manager. This preference is determined by the different funding sources available for maintenance work orders, maintenance projects, and capital projects. The cost ranges of deficiency categories can be adjusted by type of work.

In making a review of all projects, opportunities should be analyzed to "package" several projects for economies of scale. For example, roofing repairs and replacements for several buildings are commonly grouped together into a single project to allow for lower unit pricing. Similar operations, such as erecting scaffolding or suspending use of portions of buildings, also lend themselves to cost efficiencies and minimize building use inconveniences.

Intangible factors

There are other factors which do not readily lend themselves to categories but should be considered when making funding decisions.

Staff morale makes a positive contribution to overall productivity and can be influenced by sufficient space and properly functioning, well-furnished and equipped, attractive, and well-maintained facilities. Staff recruitment and retention is similarly affected by the physical appearance of facilities and the architectural qualities of buildings and site aesthetics. Accordingly, historic preservation is an emerging factor affecting priorities. Facilities in a marginal condition considered for replacement may be more valuable if retained and improved because of their importance to historic continuity or as a focal point for a community.

Organizing these categories and intangible factors into a specific set of selection guidelines enables decisions to be made based on technical evaluations and an organization's requirements.

Project Priority Levels

Priority Level	Point Value

Level I

I-1 Life Safety and Legal Compliance — 10
  a. Hazardous life safety building or site conditions that jeopardize people, programs, equipment; unless corrected will cause suspension of facilities use.
  b. Repairs, renovations, and improvements required for immediate compliance with local, state, or federal regulations.

I-2 Damage or Deterioration to Facilities — 9
Repairs, renovations, and improvements to facilities that, unless corrected, will lead to a loss of a facility.

I-3 Cost Effective Measures — 8
  a. Repairs, renovations, and improvements required to prevent serious facility deterioration and significantly higher costs if not immediately corrected.
  b. Energy conservation to reduce consumption with a rapid return on investment.

Level II

II-1 Mission Support — 7
Actions required to support functional activities.

II-2 Delayed Priority — 6
Repairs and renovations less compelling than Priority II-1.

II-3 Deferred Maintenance — 5
Deferral of repairs or renovations which will lead to major damage to a facility and loss of use, hamper building utilization, or affect economies of operation.

Level III

III-1 Project Completion — 4
Building or site improvements uncompleted because of inadequate funding or other reasons. Improvements are necessary for proper functioning, economic maintenance, and suitable appearance of new construction.

III-2 Delayed Deferred Maintenance — 3
Repairs and renovations that can be postponed.

III-3 Anticipating Actions — 2
Actions carried out in anticipation of longer range development: land acquisition, infrastructure development, and advance planning for capital projects.

III-4 Reduction in Scope — 1
Modify scope to a smaller scale or consolidate with other projects.

Figure 11.2

Management Philosophy

Two concepts influencing final priority decisions are need and risk. For example, are projects for improving the quality of the environment selected before life safety or operating economy projects?

In the final analysis, selection of priorities by management is the relative weight given to:

- the protection of plant assets;
- possible fiscal instability caused by postponing deferred maintenance or energy conservation measures;
- the visual image of the organization; and
- the risk of erosion of function and quality of the environment.

Although these matters may seem relatively intangible, they can be as debilitating as the more obvious physical consequences of deferring high priority building and site repairs.

Presenting the Audit Findings

A successful presentation to an audience on any subject begins with thorough preparation. Part of this preparation involves getting a sense of the decision-making environment, and other issues facing an approving body.

All of the technical expertise involved in preparing project budget requests have a predictable degree of failure if not effectively presented. A thoroughly prepared presentation, well-documented and imaginatively delivered, will effectively convey the message and have a greater chance of success. The presentation should relate the manner in which the approved budget or projects will improve facility operations.

The Facilities Audit can be one of the most valuable tools the facilities administrator and staff have in facilities management if it is developed and presented well. Even a flawlessly performed audit is useless unless the information can be communicated to the audience in a usable format. Conclusions and recommendations should be able to stand on their own merits.

Documentation

The documentation must be meticulous in detail because the sharpest minds in the organization will usually be present. Any references to costs, financing alternatives, or cost benefits should be thoroughly checked, as these will undergo thorough scrutiny. Expect the unexpected. Be prepared to answer the question: "What will happen if we don't do the work?" Other solutions or possible choices should always be presented for comprehensive, as well as minor, projects.

Format

Before beginning the audit process, think about what the presentation will look like. The list of projects and printed documents are the backbone of the presentation and should be presented in an appropriate format. If the report is to be submitted in print form only without oral presentation, consider what charts, graphs, and illustrations would be helpful. The report itself may be presented as a brief statement of the facts or in an extensive narrative that includes observations and commentary.

The facilities administrator should provide material which is concise, easily understandable (free of jargon), and attractively presented.

Do not oversimplify for readability, but do design the documents for easy cross-referencing.

Visual Aids

Develop a theme for the presentation: organize it so that the train of thought can be followed. Above all—keep the presentation simple and to the point.

At quarterly or annual reviews of budget requests for major maintenance and capital renewal/replacement needs, the facilities manager must play the roles of technician, counselor, and politician. Communication to the intended audience is the watchword: graphics, visual aids, and comprehensive reports should provide conclusions and recommendations that stand on their own merits. Large charts and slides or videotapes of existing conditions have a greater impact than three hours of droning prose.

Budget Review

The supporting printed materials for a budget review session should be submitted in advance to all participants. The following format for budget review sessions (see Figure 11.3) should be used to ensure the clarity and conciseness of the presentation.

1. **Title Sheet**
2. **Executive summary** of major conclusions and recommendations.
3. **A brief introduction** should explain the organization of the report. Definition of groupings of projects by funding sources should be included to ease understanding of accompanying technical material.
4. **A map of facilities** with building names.
5. **Facilities age** in periods of five or ten years.
6. **Condition rating summary** using categories of building component form.
7. **Maintenance deficiency summary** using categories of building component form.
8. **A summary of projects** identifying the building or facility, short descriptive title, and project budget. Illustrating funding sources separating operating from capital budgets can be helpful.
9. **Detailed project descriptions** presented on individual sheets for each project.

Items to Consider

Once the Facilities Audit is complete, how does one gain support for a program to correct deficiencies uncovered by the audit? Essentially, by developing an effective presentation—one that can sell conclusions and recommendations. Consider the following items when making any kind of audit presentation.

- **Overview.** Does the audit show a broad understanding of the budgetary mechanism and present a responsible fiscal position?
- **Credibility.** Does the audit show that previously allocated funds were well used? Does it take the initiative for the best use of new resources for new programs?
- **Competency.** Did the audit team and implementing staff appear professional and competent during the audit process, and in follow-up activities?
- **Thoroughness of Preparation.** Was the audit thoroughly researched, analyzed, and professionally presented? The form and content of the presentation must be an accurate presentation of the facts, objective, noncontradictory, and capable of withstanding thorough scrutiny.

FACILITIES AUDIT PRESENTATIONS

Title Sheet 1	Executive Summary 2	Map of Facilites 3

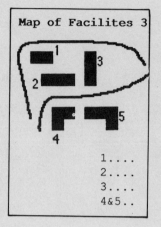

1....
2....
3....
4&5..

Facilities Age 4

Date GSF NSF
1980-
1970-79
1960-69
1950-59
1929-49
Pre-1929

Totals ____ ____

Conditions 5

Category GSF NSF
1. Unsatis
2. <25% RV
3. 25%-50% RV
4. >50% RV
5. Unsatis

Totals ____ ____

Maintenace Deficiencies 6

Category &

Mtce Wk Ord   <$
Mtce Proj   >$-$<
Capital Proj >$

Totals ____

Maintenance Deficiencies 7

Selected
Components
 # $
Roofing
Exter Clos
HVAC
Electrical
Safety

Totals ____ ____

Project Summaries 8

Title $
1...........
2...........
3...........
4...........
5...........
6...........

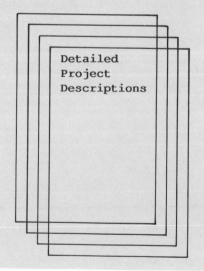

Detailed
Project
Descriptions

Figure 11.3

- **Sympathetic Senior Administrator.** The budgetary allocation process represents proposals competing for limited financial resources. Without a strong advocate, the audit findings just may be shelved. A senior administrator who understands the audit, conclusions, and recommendations is an invaluable ally in the funding and implementation process.
- **Preparation for Implementation.** The audit conclusions and recommendations must be in an immediately usable format. Administrators who will be involved in the implementation should be included in the formulation of the conclusions. Operational staff should also be involved when possible. The end result is better with these contributions and it ensures that the purpose of the audit is clear to all parties.

Summary

Following the three phases of the self-evaluation process— preparation, data collection, and presentation of findings—produces a successful Facilities Audit. The purpose and intended use should be understood. Flexibility in using the procedures is necessary to accommodate an organization's size, existing data, resources available, and time deadlines. The process described in this part of the book represents the experiences of government employees, public and private systems of higher education, and many consultants. Methods were evolved over a period of time to meet the needs of administrators and plant operations staff in different regions of the country. Procedures and Facility Rating Forms were especially designed for flexibility of manual use or adaptability for computerized applications. Applications of the self-evaluation process to your organization will benefit present as well as future functional use, employees, and the community being served.

Chapter Twelve

ESTIMATING CAPITAL RENEWAL AND REPLACEMENT

Estimating the capital budget, a primary function of the facilities manager, is a governing factor in determining an organization's budgeting and financial management planning needs. One aspect of estimating the capital budget is defining new construction projects or major additions. These are defined by scope, estimated, and scheduled as they fit into overall financial planning. A second component is estimating the company's annual budget reserve for capital renewal and replacement.

Methods for estimating capital needs are presented in this chapter.

Basic Estimating Methods

There are several different methods of estimating plant renewal and replacement needs—the life cycle method, the replacement method, and the Facilities Audit estimating method. Selecting the appropriate method requires an understanding of an organization's fiscal planning needs and available resources for estimating. The goal is to provide an adequate, realistic annual budget reserve allowance that can be used to allocate funds for specific projects. As projects are identified, perhaps through a Facilities Audit, funds are set aside and then used as required.

Annual Capital Budget

Corporate financial officers, legislators, and governing boards of nonprofit organizations set aside annual plant renewal and replacement allowances based on estimated projections. The facilities manager should be cautious in using annual allowance estimates as the sole basis for allocating funding requests. The annual budget reserve allowance is a **guideline** for policymakers in determining the general level of funding necessary for renewal and replacement as part of an operating budget. Formal budget requests should be required for individual projects. These requests should consist of project descriptions and detailed cost estimates.

Guidelines or formulas for determining annual capital renewal and replacement allowances should be based on empirical data and/or experience. However, since the annual capital budget is, at best, an order of magnitude cost, contingencies should be incorporated to accommodate variations from actual project costs.

The reserve allowance may be fully funded but not necessarily used in a fiscal year. These unused funds may be "rolled over" into the next year's annual reserve allowance.

Annual capital budgeting allowances may be prepared using formulas based on life cycle cost concepts, or calculations for replacement costs for comparable or similar facilities. Each of these methods will be explained individually later in this chapter.

Renewal and Replacement Project Estimates

Renewal and replacement projects are defined by the Facilities Audit—the assessment of existing conditions. Preliminary project estimates can be developed from the audit evaluation for entire buildings or building components by the replacement method. More refined estimates to correct an observed deficiency may be prepared using annual cost data publications such as Means *Building Construction Cost Data*. Another source is sufficiently completed design documents for specific projects correcting deficiencies, from which detailed estimates of labor, materials, and owner's costs can be estimated.

The degree of accuracy for a capital renewal and replacement project estimate is based on the time available for preparation, agency or administrative procedures for estimate submittal, and the expected actions resulting from the estimate submittal. A detailed estimate based on actual costs provided from either experienced estimators or contractors is preferred. However, when detailed information is not available or there is limited time in which to obtain complete costs, it may not be possible to provide the most accurate costs.

If budget estimates are required for a lengthy list of potential projects, the facilities manager must use the best information available to produce the most accurate estimates possible in the time frame allowed. The facilities manager must judge where to obtain the necessary information and the reliability of the sources, in view of all project factors.

Life Cycle Method

An annual allowance for renewal and replacement may be estimated based on life cycle formulas using sum-of-the-digits calculations. The principle involved in this method is that facility renewal needs increase as a facility ages. For example, an organization with an average building age of fifty years has greater renewal and replacement needs than one of twenty years. As a result, formulas for annual allowances must be weighted to compensate for age differences of facilities.

A simple straight-line projection of a building with a fifty-year life declines at the rate of two percent a year. Although a crude rule of thumb, this approach would require that two percent of a building's replacement value be set aside each year. Because buildings are made up of components and systems that age at differing rates, adjustments are made in formulas to compensate for these factors.

Sum-of-the-Digits-Method

The typical life cycle formula using the sum-of-the-digits method can be used to make these adjustments. For example, a facility with an expected fifty year life cycle is "aged" so that at the end of fifty years, it reaches its full replacement value—equal to the building age divided by 1275 (where 1275 equals the sum of $1 + 2 + 3 + 4 + \cdots 49 + 50 = 1275$). Thus, instead of generating a constant of two percent of its current renewal value each year for fifty years, a building will generate almost four percent a year (50/1275) of its current renewal value. In this way, groups of older buildings require more renewal funds than a similar group of newer buildings.

Additional adjustment factors can be used in allowance formulas to compensate for the portion of a building to be renewed at the end of its life and for renovations that have modified a facility's life. These factors can assume that at the end of a building's life, 2/3, 3/4, or 100 percent of the building value (BV) requires replacement. An example of a life cycle formula for a building annual replacement allowance is shown in Figure 12.1.

Factors used in the calculation are: the building age and current replacement value for an existing facility; or the estimated total project cost for a planned facility.

This technique can be estimated by hand or computer spreadsheet for each individual building. A compilation of such calculations for all buildings or facilities will produce an estimated annual operating budget and capital project budget. As stated in the previous section, this renewal allowance represents a pool of funds to be allocated later for individual projects, performed in order of priority.

Annual Replacement Allowance = 2/3BV × BA/1275

where:

Annual Replacement Allowance = the funding which should be allocated annually
2/3 = The building renewal constant for an assumed replacement
BV = The building value determined by updating the original construction cost to a current replacement value
BA = The building age as corrected for either partial or total building renewal
1275 = The age-weighting constant based on a 50-year life

Example:

1. An unrenovated building constructed in 1965 at a cost of $1,000,000 has a current replacement value (1989) of $3.1 million:

Annual allowance = 2/3BV × BA/1275
1989 Allowance = 2/3 $3,100,000 × 24/1275
= $2,067,000 × 0.01882
= $38,901

Life Cycle Formula

Figure 12.1

189

Component Method

An alternate to the sum-of-the-digits methods "ages" each major component of a building to determine an annual replacement allowance. Empirical studies using this method produce a range of 1-1/2 to 3 percent of current replacement value. This figure serves as a useful guideline in estimating an organization's overall budget needs for capital renewal and replacement.

Replacement Index Method

A more refined approach than formulas involves the use of replacement cycles for renewing building components and systems to produce a replacement index. The index is expressed as a percent value equivalent to the portion of a facility that must be replaced annually and includes the following factors:

- **Facility type**—subsystems and associated costs vary widely across the range of building types.
- **Date of construction**—the original date of construction and date of major additions and renovations affect renewal funding needs.
- **Facility subsystems**—the quantity and quality of installed subsystems within a facility will determine replacement requirements.
- **Subsystem life cycles**—predictable life of a subsystem will determine when future replacement requirements will occur.
- **Subsystem cost**—unit replacement cost for subsystems affect future requirements.

A replacement index for the purposes of computing an annual renewal allowance for a facility uses the following steps:

1. Define building systems
2. Estimate system costs
3. Calculate system percentage of total construction
4. Estimate system life cycle
5. Calculate replacement index

A sample calculation of a replacement index for a low-rise (one to four story) office building is shown in Figure 12.2 and follows the steps outlined below.

Step One—Define Building Systems

The building components outlined in Column One of Figure 12.2 are those used in *Means Square Foot Costs* for a similar building type. A uniform listing of building components should be used for consistency in the factors for developing replacement indexes for various building types.

Steps Two and Three—Estimate System Costs and System Percent of Total Construction

Building component costs are obtained from *Means Square Foot Costs* for a similar building type. The percent of total construction is calculated by dividing the cost of each component into the total project cost.

Step Four—Estimate System Life Cycle

Various sources provide the average number of years before replacement or major repairs are required, to estimate the life of a component. A secondary set of calculations may be required for a facility with a major renovation.

Step Five—Calculate Replacement Index

The final step in the calculation is to divide the percent of total construction (Column 3 in Figure 12.2) by the replacement life (Column 4) to produce a replacement index for each component (Column 5). The total of the component indexes results in a replacement index or annual renewal allowance of 2.61 percent of the current replacement value of the building.

Analyses using this procedure can be performed for different building types and a summary replacement index developed for an organization's facilities. This final amount provides a guide for annual capital budgeting of renewal and replacement needs.

Facilities Audit Cost Estimating

The Facilities Audit building analysis worksheets presented in Chapter 9 provide additional sources for estimating renewal and replacement capital needs. The concept of auditing was described as noting observed deficiencies with a "condition rating" noted for building components. The information from these ratings can be converted to a "replacement" estimate of renewal and replacement capital needs for individual components and summarized for an entire building, for all similar components in an organization's facilities, and for all company facilities.

A choice was also presented to enter an estimate of costs for correcting an observed deficiency. Cost data books published by R.S. Means Company, Inc., can be used to obtain cost estimates of labor and material requirements for a specific project. Summaries of cost estimates can be prepared for actual costs provided by a facilities planning department, by contractors, or by consultants.

The replacement method of estimating component costs and total building costs using the Facilities Audit is shown in Figure 12.3. This is not a substitute for a detailed project estimate based on quantities of labor and material. However, it serves as a useful tool in providing order of magnitude costs for comparing projects.

The rating on an individual Component Rating Form in the example for foundations is based on an evaluation on a scale from 0.0 to 1.0, from unsatisfactory to a satisfactory condition. This rating is called a **Condition Value Multiplier**. The bottom line of each rating form, Component Rating (Line D), contains a space for the product of the possible rating, to be multiplied by the Condition Value Multiplier. Steps in estimating the costs to correct a deficiency in the example in Figure 12.3 are:

1. Building total replacement value is $1,000,000.
2. Possible rating for foundations is 3 percent of the total replacement value.
3. Replacement value for foundations is 3% × $1,000,000 = $30,000.
4. Condition rating of foundations from inspection is 1.5 of a possible rating of 3, meaning that it requires 50% of replacement value to correct deficiencies.
5. Cost estimate for correcting deficiency at 50% replacement value = .5 × $30,000 = $15,000.

REPLACEMENT INDEX FOR A ONE TO FOUR STORY OFFICE BUILDING

Column 1	Column 2	Column 3	Column 4	Column 5
BUILDING COMPONENT	Cost per Gross Square Feet	Percent of Total Constr.	Average Year Before Replacement Value	Replacement Index = % per Year of Total
1. Foundations	$ 1.18	2.25	100	.023
2. Substructure	.85	1.61	100	.016
3. Superstructure	5.73	10.90	100	.109
4. Exterior Closure	5.22	9.93	50	.199
5. Roofing	.90	1.71	15	.114
6. Int.Constr.	11.88	22.61	20	1.130
7. Conveying	1.99	3.79	25	.152
8. Mechanical	8.74	16.63	25	.665
9. Electrical	6.22	11.84	40	.296
10. Equipment	-	-	-	
11. Spec. Constr.	-	-	-	
12. Site work	-	-	-	
Subtotal	$42.71			
Gen Conditions (15%)	$ 6.41	12.20		
Arch Fees (7%)	$ 3.43	6.53		
Total Building Cost	$52.55	100.00		

REPLACEMENT INDEX (percent of replacement value) = 2.70

Figure 12.2

B 1.1 PRIMARY SYSTEMS – FOUNDATIONS

FAC # __1__   FACILITY NAME __Office Bldg.__ REPLACEMENT

DATE __7/8/89__ INSPECTOR __H.H.K.__   VALUE $ __30,000__

A. SYSTEM DESCRIPTION

(a) Footings:
Individual Footings & Piers __✓__ Continuous Footings_____
Grade Beams_____   Piles_____   Caissons_____
(b) Foundation Wall Materials:
Steel _____ Concrete Cast-in-place __✓__
Concrete Block _____ Other _____
(c) Waterproofing and Underdrain
Coating _____ Membrane _____ Board __✓__

B. COMPONENT EVALUTION

(a) Condition   (b) Deficiency   (c) Priority
Rating   Report   Rating
1._____   1._____   1._____
2._____   2._____   2.__✓__
3.__✓__   3.__✓__   3._____
4._____   4._____   4._____
5._____   Total $ _____

C. MAINTENANCE DEFICIENCY COMMENTS

Cracks from settling. Estimated at $10,000.
Moisture on inside northeast corner of
foundation wall.

D. COMPONENT RATING: (   ) x (   ) = _____
                          Possible   Condition   Rating
                          Rating   Value
                                        Multiplier

Figure 12.3

B 1 BUILDING EVALUATION SUMMARY

I. BUILDING INFORMATION

FAC #_____ FACILITY NAME _____ LOCATION _____

DATE _____ INSPECTOR _____

YEAR CONST, ADDN_____

GROSS SQ FT _____NET SQ FT _____

ORIGINAL COST $_____ REPLACEMENT COST $_____

II. COMPONENT RATING

COMPONENT	RATING Possible	Actual
Primary Systems	(_____)	
1. Foundations	_____	_____
2. Substructure	_____	_____
3. Superstructure	_____	_____
4. Exterior Closure	_____	_____
5. Roofing	_____	_____
Secondary Systems	(_____)	
6. Partitions and Doors	_____	_____
7. Walls & Finishes	_____	_____
8. Floors & Finishes	_____	_____
9. Ceilings & Finishes	_____	_____
Service Systems	(_____)	
10. Conveying	_____	_____
11. Mechanical: Plumbing	_____	_____
12. Mechanical: Heating	_____	_____
13. Mechanical: Cooling & Ventilation	_____	_____
14. Electrical: Service & Distribution	_____	_____
15. Electrical: Lighting & Power	_____	_____
Safety Standards	(_____)	
16. Safety Standards	_____	_____
Functional Standards	(_____)	
17A. Suitability & Adaptability	_____	_____
17B. Use Considerations	_____	_____

III. BUILDING RATING SUMMARY

Building Rating _____   (_____)   (_____)

Figure 12.3 (*continued*)

Estimating costs for correcting total deficiencies using the Building Evaluation Summary is also shown in Figure 12.3, and proceeds through the following steps:

1. Building Total Replacement Value equals $1,000,000.
2. The Actual Rating for the building is 70%.
3. The cost of correcting deficiencies is equal to the possible rating (100) minus the actual rating (70): $100\% - 70\% = 30\%$ of replacement value.
4. The cost estimate for correcting the deficiency at 30% replacement value equals $.30 \times \$1,000,000 = \$300,000$.

Cost estimates obtained from a Facilities Audit using the replacement method is a more accurate approach than formula and life cycle estimates. The costs totalled from deficiency estimates using labor and material quantities is the most accurate method of estimating and is recommended where resources and time are available. When selecting any particular method, the level of capital budgeting and information needs should be considered.

Sample Estimates

Comparisons of results from a hypothetical building example illustrate the range in cost estimates by the suggested methods for renewal and replacement. The example used in the preceding paragraphs is a four story office building constructed in 1965 at a cost of $1 million (and never renovated) with a current replacement value (1989) of $3.1 million. Estimates for an annual renewal allowance for the same building using different methods appear below.

Current Replacement Value

The range for an estimated annual renewal allowance uses 1-1/2 to 3 percent of the current replacement value (CRV). The calculation results in the following range:

Current Replacement Value	= $3,100,000
Annual Renewal Allowance Percent Range	= (.015 to .03)
Annual Renewal Allowance	= CRV (.015 to .03)
	= $3,100,000 (.015 to .03)
	= $46,500 to $93,000

Life Cycle Method

Calculation using life cycles and a sum of the digits method described in the Life Cycle Method section of this chapter resulted in an annual renewal allowance of $26,500.

Replacement Index

The replacement index developed in Figure 12.3 produced a replacement index of 2.61. This is equivalent to an annual renewal allowance. A calculation using the index is made as follows:

Annual Renewal Allowance	= CRV (2.61)
	= $3,100,000 (2.61)
Annual Renewal Allowance	= $80,910

The variations in these estimates show some of the shortcomings of preparing an annual renewal allowance without doing a detailed Facilities Audit. Each method is slightly more accurate than the preceding one because of the use of factors more specific to the facility being estimated. As estimates of capital renewal and replacement, they are used to establish order of magnitude needs for renewal allowances. However, they are not as accurate as estimates obtained from a Facilities Audit.

A Final Word

An organization's awareness that inadequate renewal and replacement funding has created a set of deteriorating plant conditions should lead to a Facilities Audit. The results of the audit produce a list of capital and maintenance projects that can be funded to improve plant conditions. Facilities managers should impress upon policy-makers that one time elimination of deferred maintenance does not solve the problems of renewal, and replacement is mandatory to prevent future accumulation of deferred maintenance. Establishing an appropriate level of funding in the beginning of a deferred maintenance program may have to include "catch-up costs." As needs are reduced to manageable amounts, the operating budget can accommodate priorities as they are identified. The end result is a program that maintains facilities in good repair, efficient to operate and maintain, and functionally adequate for an organization's mission.

▮Appendix

Forms and checklists for performing the Facilities Audit are provided in the Appendix for each building system, and for functional performance. The component forms have four major parts: A. System Description, B. Component Evaluation, C. Maintenance Deficiency Comments, and D. Component Rating. While A, C, and D are self-explanatory, Section B uses the following rating system:

(a) Condition Rating	(b) Deficiency Comment	(c) Priority Rating
1 = Satisfactory	1 = No Work	1 = Emergency
2 = Remodeling A = < 25% RV*	2 = Maintenance Work Order	2 = Urgent
3 = Remodeling B = > 25% < 50% RV*	3 = Maintenance Project	3 = Routine
4 = Remodeling C = > 50% RV*	4 = Capital Project	4 = Deferred
5 = Unsatisfactory/Demolition		
* = replacement value		

A.1 BUILDING DATA SUMMARY

Building Number	Building Name	Building Use*	Location/ Address	Ownership** Own/Lea/O-L

*Principal and Special Uses

** Own = Owned
Lea = Leased
O-L = Owned/Leased

A.2 PROPERTY FILE

Building Data

1. Organization Name _____

2. Approved by
   Name _____ Title _____ Date _____

3. Building Number _____

4. Property Name _____

5. Property Address _____

6. Property Main Use/Special Use _____

7. Gross Area (Sq. Ft.) _____

8. Net Area (Sq. Ft.) _____

9. Type of Ownership: _____ Owned _____ Lea _____ O-L _____

10. Book Value $_____ Year Appraised _____

11. Replacement Value $_____

12. Year Constructed/Major Additions _____

13. Year Acquired _____

Land Data

14. Type of Ownership: _____ Owned _____ Lea _____ O-L _____

15. Book Value _____ Year Appraised _____
16. Year Acquired _____
17. Size in Acres _____
18. Market Values _____

Notes: _____
        _____
        _____
        _____
        _____

B1 BUILDING EVALUATION SUMMARY

I. BUILDING INFORMATION

FAC #_____ FACILITY NAME _____ LOCATION _____

DATE _____ INSPECTOR _____

YEAR CONST, ADDN_____

GROSS SQ FT _____NET SQ FT _____

ORIGINAL COST $_____ REPLACEMENT COST $_____

II. COMPONENT RATING

COMPONENT	RATING Possible	Actual
Primary Systems	(_____)	
1. Foundations		
2. Substructure	____	____
3. Superstructure	____	____
4. Exterior Closure	____	____
5. Roofing	____	____
	____	
Secondary Systems	(_____)	
6. Partitions and Doors		
7. Walls & Finishes	____	____
8. Floors & Finishes	____	____
9. Ceilings & Finishes	____	____
	____	
Service Systems	(_____)	
10. Conveying	____	
11. Mechanical: Plumbing	____	____
12. Mechanical: Heating	____	____
13. Mechanical: Cooling & Ventilation	____	____
14. Electrical: Service & Distribution	____	____
15. Electrical: Lighting & Power	____	____
	____	
Safety Standards	(_____)	
16. Safety Standards		
	____	____
Functional Standards	(_____)	
17A. Suitability & Adaptability		
17B. Use Considerations	____	____
	____	____

III. BUILDING RATING SUMMARY

Building Rating _____   (_____)   (_____)

B1.1 PRIMARY SYSTEMS – FOUNDATIONS

FAC #_____   FACILITY NAME_____REPLACEMENT

DATE_____   INSPECTOR_____VALUE $_____

A. SYSTEM DESCRIPTION

   (a) Footings:
       Individual Footings & Piers_____ Continuous Footings_____
       Grade Beams_____   Piles_____   Caissons_____
   (b) Foundation Wall Materials:
       Steel _____ Concrete Cast-in-place _____
       Concrete Block _____ Other _____
   (c) Waterproofing and Underdrain
       Coating _____ Membrane _____ Board _____

B. COMPONENT EVALUTION

   (a) Condition   (b) Deficiency   (c) Priority
       Rating   Report   Rating
       1._____   1._____   1._____
       2._____   2._____   2._____
       3._____   3._____   3._____
       4._____   4._____   4._____
       5._____   Total $ _____

C. MAINTENANCE DEFICIENCY COMMENTS

   _____
   _____
   _____
   _____
   _____

D. COMPONENT RATING: (_____) x (_____) = _____
                          Possible   Condition   Rating
                          Rating   Value
                                        Multiplier

B1.1 FOUNDATIONS - INSPECTION CHECKLIST

Deficiencies	Causes
Settlement, alignment changes or cracks	Soils - changes in load bearing capacity due to skrinkage, erosion, or compaction. Adjacent construction undermining foundations. Reduced soil cover resulting in frost exposure. Design loads - building equipment loads exceeding design loads. Vibration from heavy equipment requiring isolated foundations. Structural or occupancy changes - inadequate bearing capacities. Foundation settling. Earthquake resistance non-functioning.
Moisture penetration	Water table changes - inadequate drainage. Ineffective drains or sump pump/sump pits. Roof drainage - storm sewer connections inadequate or defective. Installation of roof drain restrictors, gutters, and downspouts where required. Surface drainage - exterior grades should slope away from building and structures. Utilities - broken or improperly functioning utility service lines or drains. Leakage - wall cracks, opening of construction joints, inadequate or defective waterproofing. Condensation - inadequate ventilation, vapor barrier, and/or dehumidificaion.
Temperature changes	Insulation - improperly selected for insulating value, fire ratings, and vermin resistance.
Surface material deterioration	Concrete, masonry, or stucco - spalling, corrosion of reinforcing, moisture penetration, or chemical reaction between cement and soil. Steel or other ferrous metals - corrosion due to moisture or contact with acid-bearing soils. Wood - decay due to moisture or insect infestation.
Openings deterioration	Non-functioning of doors, windows, hatchways, and stairways. Utilities penetration due to damage, weather, wear, or other cause.

B1.2 PRIMARY SYSTEMS – SUBSTRUCTURE

FAC #_____ FACILITY NAME _____ REPLACEMENT
DATE_____ INSPECTOR_____ VALUE $_____

A. SYSTEM DESCRIPTION
    (a) Slab on Grade
       Plain_____
       Reinforced _____
    (b) Special Substructures
      _____

B. COMPONENT EVALUTION
(a) Condition Rating	(b) Deficiency Report	(c) Priority Rating
1._____	1._____	1._____
2._____	2._____	2._____
3._____	3._____	3._____
4._____	4._____	4._____
5._____	Total $_____	

C. MAINTENANCE DEFICIENCY COMMENTS
_____
_____
_____
_____
_____
_____
_____
_____

D. COMPONENT RATING: (_____) (_____) = _____
                 Possible   Condition   Rating
                 Rating   Value
                         Multiplier

B1.2 SUBSTRUCTURE INSPECTION CHECKLIST

Deficiencies	Causes
Floors, concrete - Cracking or arching	Skrinkage, settlement or subsoil, inadequate drainage, movement in exterior walls, or frost heave. Improper compaction of base. Erosion of base. Heaving from hydraulic pressure.
Floors, wood - rotting or arching	Excessive dampness or insect infestation. Leak in building exterior. Lack of ventilation.
Wall deterioration	Concrete or masonry (see B1.1 Foundations)
Crawl space ventilaiton and maintenance	Inadequate air circulation due to blockage of openings in foundation walls. Moisture barrier ineffective. Pest control, housekeeping, and proper drainage.

B1.3 PRIMARY SYSTEMS – SUPERSTRUCTURE

FAC #_____ FACILITY NAME _____ REPLACEMENT
DATE _____ INSPECTOR_____ VALUE $_____

A. SYSTEM DESCRIPTION
    (a) Columns and Beams
        Concrete-in-place _____ Precast Concrete _____
        Steel _____ Steel Fireproofing _____
        Wood _____ Other _____
    (b) Floors
        Concrete Slab _____ Precast Concrete _____
        Metal Deck _____ Metal Deck w/Conc Fill _____
        Composite Beam, Deck & Slab _____
        Wood _____ Other _____
    (c) Roof System
        Flat _____ Pitched _____
        Concrete _____Steel _____Wood_____Other_____
    (d) Pre engineered _____
    (e) Other _____

B. COMPONENT EVALUATION

(a) Condition Rating	(b) Deficiency Report	(c) Priority Rating
1._____	1._____	1._____
2._____	2._____	2._____
3._____	3._____	3._____
4._____	4._____	4._____
5._____	Total $ _____	

C. MAINTENANCE DEFICIENCY COMMENTS

_____
_____
_____
_____
_____
_____

D. COMPONENT RATING: (_____) x (_____) = _____
                  Possible   Condition   Rating
                  Rating   Multiplier
                             Value

B1.3 SUPERSTRUCTURE - INSPECTION CHECKLIST

The primary materials encountered in the superstructure inspection are concrete, steel, and wood. Typical observations of deficiencies will be observed by: failures in the exterior closure systems of exterior walls, openings, and roofs; cracks; movement of materials; moisture penetration; and discoloration. The exterior visual survey will detect failures of surface materials or at openings that will require further inspection to determine whether the cause was the superstructure system.

Concrete is a composite material and subject to more types of deterioration than steel or wood. Observed failures can originate by incorrect design and construction techniques not readily detected by visual inspections. Analysis of original design criteria and materials by laboratory testing may be required to determine the causes of problems.

Deficiencies	Causes
Concrete (Columns, Walls, and Floor and Roof Slabs)	
Overall alignment	Settlement; design and construction techniques. Under designed for loading conditions (see B1.1 Foundations).
Deflection	Expansion and/or contraction; changes in design loads. Original design deficient. Original materials deficient.
Surface Conditions	
Cracks	Inadequate design and/or construction; changes in design loads; stress concentration; extreme temperature changes; secondary effects of freeze-thaw.
Scaling, Spalls, and Pop-outs	Extreme temperature changes; reinforcement corrosion; environmental conditions; mechancial damage; poor materials.
Stains	Chemical reaction of reinforcing; reaction of materials in concrete mixture; environmental conditions.
Exposed reinforcing	Corrosion of steel; insufficient cover; mechanical damage.
Steel (Structural Members, Stairs, and Connections	
Overall alignment	Settlement; design and construction techniques; improper fabrication.
Deflection or cracking	Expansion and/or contraction; changes in design loads; fatigue due to vibration or impact.

Corrosion   Electro-chemcial reaction; failure of
                                   protective coating; excessive moisture
                                   exposure.

Surface deterioration   Excessive wear.

Wood (Structural Members and Connections)
Overall alignment   Settlement; design and construction
                                   techniques.

Deflection or cracking   Expansion and/or contraction; changes in
                                   design loads; fatigue due to vibration or
                                   impact; failure of compression members.
                                   Poor construction techniques.
                                   General material failure.

Rot (Decay)   Direct contact with moisture;
                                   condensation; omission or deterioration
                                   of vapor barrier.
                                   Poor construction techniques.
                                   Damage from rodents or insects.

B1.4 PRIMARY SYSTEMS – EXTERIOR CLOSURE

FAC #_____ FACILITY NAME _____ REPLACEMENT
DATE _____ INSPECTOR _____ VALUE $_____

A. SYSTEM DESCRIPTION

(A) Walls
  Concrete_____ Masonry_____ Metal Siding_____
  Wood/siding_____ Other_____

(b) Finishes
  Stucco_____ Paint_____ Other_____

(c) Doors
  Wood_____ Steel_____ Alum_____ Other_____

(d) Windows (type: fixed, double hung, casement, etc.)
  Wood_____ Steel_____ Alum_____ Other_____

(e) Shading Devices
  Types_____

B. COMPONENT EVALUATION

(a) Condition Rating   (b) Deficiency Report   (c) Priority Rating
  1._____   1._____   1._____
  2._____   2._____   2._____
  3._____   3._____   3._____
  4._____   4._____   4._____
  5._____   Total $ _____

C. MAINTENANCE DEFICIENCY COMMENTS

_____
_____
_____
_____
_____
_____
_____
_____

D. COMPONENT RATING: (_____) x (_____) = _____

              Possible   Condition   Rating
              Rating   Value
                              Multiplier

B1.4 EXTERIOR CLOSURE INSPECTION CHECKLIST

General Inspection

Overall appearance

Displacement

Paint conditions

Caulking

Window & door fit

Flashing condition

Material integrity

Cracks

Evidence of moisture

Construction joints

Hardware condition

Exterior Walls

Wood (Shingles, weatherboard siding, plywood).

Check for:

Paint or surface treatment condition

Rot or decay

Moisture penetration

Loose, cracked, warped, or broken boards and shingles.

Concrete, Masonry, and Tile (Concrete, brick, concrete masonry units, structural tile, glazed tile, stucco, stone).

Check for:

Settlement

Structural frame movement causing cracks

Construction and expansion joints

Surface deterioration

Parapet movement

Condition of caulking and mortar

Efflorescence and staining

Tightness of fasteners

Metal (Corrugated iron or steel, aluminum, enamel coated steel, protected metals).

Check for:

Settlement

Condition of bracing

Tightness of fasteners

Flashings

Stuctural frame movement

Surface damage due to impact

Caulking

Corrosion

Finishes (Mineral products, fiberglass, polyester resins, and plastics).

Check for:

Settlement

Surface damage due to impact

Stains

Adhesion to substrate

Flashings

Structural frame movement

Cracks

Fasteners

Caulking

Windows and Doors
Check for:

Frame fitting

Paint or surface finish

Hardware and operating parts

Cleanliness

Rot or corrision

Frame and molding condition

Putty and weatherstripping

Security

Material condition (glass, wood and metal panels)

Screens and storm windows

Shading Devices
Check for:

Material conditions

Cleanliness

Operations

B1.5 PRIMARY SYSTEMS - ROOFING

FAC #_____ FACILITY NAME _____ REPLACEMENT

DATE _____ INSPECTOR_____ VALUE $_____

A. SYSTEM DESCRIPTION

(a) Roof Covering

Built-up_____Single Ply Membrane_____Metal_____

Preformed Met_____ Shingle or Tile_____

Other_____

(b) Flashing

Base & Counter_____Cap_____Through Wall_____

Valley & Ridge_____ Vent_____ Chimney_____

(c) Gravel Stop & Edge Strips

Type _____

(d) Drainage

Gutters_____Drains_____Scuppers_____

Downspouts_____

(e) Projections

Pipes _____ Stacks _____ Bracing _____

Skylights _____ Other _____

B. COMPONENT EVALUATION

(a) Condition Rating	(b) Deficiency Report	(c) Priority Rating
1._____	1._____	1._____
2._____	2._____	2._____
3._____	3._____	3._____
4._____	4._____	4._____
5._____	Total $ _____	

C. MAINTENANCE DEFICIENCY COMMENTS

_____

_____

_____

_____

_____

_____

_____

_____

D. COMPONENT RATING: (   ) x (   ) = _____

       Possible   Condition   Rating

       Rating   Value

                         Multiplier

B1.5 ROOFING INSPECTION CHECKLIST

General Appearance
Good_____ Fair_____ Poor_____

Watertightness
Evidence of leaks on undersurface_____   Surface weathering_____
Faulty material_____   Faulty design_____
Faulty application_____   Standing water_____
Weather damage_____   Mechanical damage_____
Fastening failure_____   Flashing failure_____

Roofing Surface
Built Up (Felt or bitumen surfacing)
Adhesion_____   Moisture meter readings____
Bare areas_____   Blisters, wrinkles_____
Cracks, holes, tears_____   Fish mouths_____
Alligatoring_____   Ballast_____

Single Ply (Thermosetting, thermoplastic, composites)
Adhesion_____   Moisture meter readings____
Bare areas_____   Blister, wrinkles_____
Cracks_____   Holes, tears_____
Seam conditions_____   Protective coating_____
Ballast_____

Metal Roofing (Preformed, formed)
Corrosion (%)_____   Protective coating_____
Seams_____   Cracks or breaks_____
Holes_____   Expansion joints_____

Shingles & Tiles (Metal, clay, mission, concrete, or others)
Disintegration_____   Broken or cracked (%)_____
Missing (%)_____   Fasteners_____
Underlayment_____

Wood shingles
Cracked_____   Curled_____
Missing (%)_____

Flashings

Deterioration_____   Open joints_____
Holes or damage_____   Anchoring_____
Protective coating_____

Drainage

Alignment_____   Free flowing_____
Clamping rings secure_____   Screens_____
Corrosion_____

B1.6 SECONDARY STYSTEMS - PARTITIONS & DOORS

FAC #_____ FACILITY NAME_____ REPLACEMENT
DATE _____ INSPECTOR _____ VALUE $_____

A. SYSTEM DESCRIPTION
    (a) Partition Classification
        Rigid_____ Load Bearing_____Movable_____
    (b) Partition Framing
        Concrete Block_____Wood Stud_____Metal Stud_____
        Structural Tile_____Rated_____Other_____
    (c) Movable Walls
        Folding Ptn_____Operable Walls_____Relocatable Ptn_____
    (d) Special partitions & Walls
        Toilet_____Screen Walls_____Gate_____Other_____
    (e) Wall Material
        Plaster_____Plaster Board_____Glass _____Plywood_____
        Paneling_____Trim & Wainscot_____Tile/Glazed_____Other_____
    (f) Interior Doors & Frames
        Met Door/Met Frame_____Wood Door/Wood Frame_____
        Glazing_____Rollup_____Sliding_____Other_____
    (g) Hardware
        Door Closers_____Lock Sets_____Hinges_____Kick/Push Plates_____
        Thresholds_____Sliding Door Equip_____Panic Devices_____
        Security & Detection_____Automatic Openers_____Other_____

B. COMPONENT EVALUATION

(a) Condition Rating	(b) Deficiency Report	(c) Priority Rating
1._____	1._____	1._____
2._____	2._____	2._____
3._____	3._____	3._____
4._____	4._____	4._____
5._____	Total $_____	

C. MAINTENANCE DEFICIENCY COMMENTS

_____
_____
_____
_____
_____
_____

D. COMPONENET RATING: (   ) x (   ) = _____
                Possible   Condition   Rating
                Rating   Value
                                Multiplier

B1.6 PARITIONS & DOORS INSPECTION CHECKLIST

General Inspection

Strength & stability_____   Physical condition_____

Acoustical quality_____   Adaptability_____

Maintainability_____   Code compliance_____

Wall Material

  Deficiencies   **Causes**

      Cracks_____   Settlement

      Holes_____   Defective material

      Looseness_____   Operational abuse or vibrations

      Missing segments_____   Environmental attack

      Water stains_____   Moisture

      Joints_____   Structural expansion or
                                             contraction

      Surface appearance_____   Wind pressure

Hardware

      Overall condition_____   Appearance_____

      Keying system_____   Operations_____

      Fit_____   Locksets_____

      Cylinders_____   Panic devices_____

      Maintainability_____   Security operations_____

B1.7 SECONDARY SYSTEMS – WALLS & FINISHES

FAC #_____ FACILITY NAME_____ REPLACEMENT
DATE _____ INSPECTOR _____ VALUE $_____

A. SYSTEM DESCRIPTION
(a) Paint _____
(b) Wall Coatings _____
(c) Wall Coverings _____
(d) Paneling
   Prefinished _____ Plank _____
(e) Cork_____
(f) Wallpaper _____
(g) Ceramic Tile _____
(h) Trim & Wainscot_____
(i) Decoration_____
(j) Glass _____

B. COMPONENT EVALUATION

(a) Condition Rating	(b) Deficiency Report	(c) Priority Rating
1._____	1._____	1._____
2._____	2._____	2._____
3._____	3._____	3._____
4._____	4._____	4._____
5._____	Total $_____	

C. MAINTENANCE DEFICIENCY COMMENTS

_____
_____
_____
_____
_____
_____
_____

D. COMPONENT RATING: (   )   x   (   )   =   _____

| Possible Rating | Condition Value Multiplier | Rating |

B1.7 WALLS & FINISHES INSPECTION CHECKLIST

(See also B1.6 Partitions & Doors)

GENERAL INSPECTION

    Overall Appearange
        Good _____ Fair _____ Poor _____
    Evidence of moisture _____
    Settlement _____
    Cracks _____
    Surface condition _____
    Cleanliness _____
    Stains _____
    Discoloration _____

PAINT

    Repainting necessary _____
    Peeling, cracking, flaking _____
    Reflectivity _____
    Maintainability _____

COVERINGS & COATINGS

    Replacement necessary _____
    Peeling _____
    Rips, tears _____
    Holes _____
    Adhesion _____
    Seams _____

INTERIOR GLAZING

    Cracks _____
    Seals _____
    Frame condition _____
    Missing panes _____
    Shading devices _____

B1.8 SECONDARY STYSTEMS - FLOORS & FINISHES

FAC #_____ FACILITY NAME_____ REPLACEMENT
DATE _____ INSPECTOR _____ VALUE $_____

A. SYSTEM DESCRIPTION

(a) Carpet
Tile_____Tufted_____Material_____
(b) Composition
Epoxy_____Synthetic (type_____ Other_____
(c) Concrete Topping
Granolithic_____ Abrasive_____Expoxy Aggregate_____
Paint_____
(d) Resilient
VAT_____Linoleum_____Vinyl_____
Rubber_____ Cork_____
(e) Ceramic Tile_____
(f) Masonry_____
(g) Terrazzo_____
(h) Wood_____
(i) Metal_____

B. COMPONENT EVALUATION

(a) Condition Rating	(b) Deficiency Report	(c) Priority Rating
1._____	1._____	1._____
2._____	2._____	2._____
3._____	3._____	3._____
4._____	4._____	4._____
5._____	Total $_____	

C. MAINTENANCE DEFICIENCY COMMENTS

_____
_____
_____
_____
_____
_____

D. COMPONENT RATING: (   ) x (   ) = _____

Possible   Condition   Rating
Rating   Value
               Multiplier

B1.8 FLOORS & FINISHES INSPECTION CHECKLIST

General Inspection
    Overall Appearance
        Good_____Fair_____Poor_____
    Evidence of moisture_____
    Visible settlement_____
    Irregular surface_____
    Tripping hazards_____
    Handicapped hazards_____
    Replacement necessary_____

Carpet (Tufted, tile)
    Age_____   Wear_____
    Stains_____   Discoloration_____
    Holes, tears_____   Seam conditions_____

Resilient (Asphalt tile, cork tile, linoleum, rubber, vinyl)
    Broken tiles_____   Loose tiles_____
    Shrinkage_____   Lifting, cupping_____
    Fading_____   Cuts, holes_____
    Porosity_____

Masonry (Stone, brick)
    Cracks_____   Deterioration_____
    Joints_____   Stains_____
    Porosity_____   Sealing_____

Monolithic Topping (Concrete, granolithic, terrazzo, magnesite)
    Cracks_____   Porosity_____
    Joints_____   Sealing _____

Wood (Plank, strips, block, parquet)
    Skrinkage_____   Cupping, warpage_____
    Excessive wear_____   Uneveness_____
    Decay_____   Sealing_____

B1.9 SECONDARY SYSTEMS – CEILINGS & FINISHES

FAC # _____ FACILITY NAME _____ REPLACEMENT

DATE _____ INSPECTOR _____ VALUE $ _____

A. SYSTEM DESCRIPTION

    (a) System Type

        Exposed _____ Applied to Structure _____ Suspended _____

    (b) Materials

        Drywall _____ Plaster _____ Mineral Fiber _____

        Metal Pan _____ Tiles _____ Board _____

        Luminous Panels _____ Other _____

    (c) Finishes

        Paint _____ Mineral Fiber _____ Fabric _____

        Prefinished _____ Other _____

    (d) Openings & Inserts

        Air Distribution _____ Lighting Fixtures _____

        Access Panels _____ Skylights _____ Fire Protection _____

        Other _____

B. COMPONENT EVALUATION

    (a) Condition Rating (b) Deficiency Report (c) Priority Rating

    1. _____   1. _____   1. _____

    2. _____   2. _____   2. _____

    3. _____   3. _____   3. _____

    4. _____   4. _____   4. _____

    5. _____   Total $ _____

C. MAINTENANCE DEFICIENCY COMMENTS

_____

_____

_____

_____

_____

D. COMPONENT RATING: (   ) x (   ) = _____

                   Possible   Condition   Rating

                   Rating   Value

                                Multiplier

B1.9 CEILINGS & FINISHES INSPECTION CHECKLIST

(See also B1.7 WALLS & FINISHES)

General Inspection

Overall appearance
    Good _____ Fair _____ Poor _____
Settlement or sagging _____
Alignment _____
Attachment _____
Evidence of moisture _____
Stains, discoloration _____
Missing units _____
Suitability _____
Acoustic quality _____
Code compliance _____

Exposed Systems (Unpainted, painted, spray-on, decorative)

Cracks _____
Surface deterioration _____
Missing elements _____
Adhesion _____

Applied to Structure & Suspended

General Condition:
    Good _____ Fair _____ Poor _____
Fasteners _____
Trim condition _____
Openings:
        Panels _____   Inserts _____
        Lighting fixtures _____   Air distribution _____
        Fire protection _____   Other _____

B1.10 SERVICE SYSTEMS — CONVEYING

FAC # _____ FACILITY NAME _____ REPLACEMENT

DATE _____ INSPECTOR _____ VALUE $ _____

A. SYSTEM DESCRIPTION

(a) Elevators
Number _____ Type(s) _____
Speed _____ Capacity (lbs)_____
Control Type(s) _____

(b) Lifts & Hoists
Number _____ Type _____

(c) Moving Stairs & Walks
Number _____ Type _____

(d) Conveyors
Number _____ Type _____

(e) Pneumatic Tubes
Number _____ Type _____

B. COMPONENT EVALUATION

(a) Condition Rating   (b) Deficiency Report   (c) Priority Rating
1. _____   1. _____   1. _____
2. _____   2. _____   2. _____
3. _____   3. _____   3. _____
4. _____   4. _____   4. _____
5. _____   Total $ _____

C. MAINTENANCE DEFICIENCY COMMENTS

_____
_____
_____
_____
_____

D. COMPONENT RATING: (_____) x (_____) = _____

Possible   Condition   Rating
Rating   Value
                  Multiplier

B1.10 CONVEYING INSPECTION CHECKLIST

General Inspection (Passenger Conveying)

Maintenance history _____

    Inspection frequency _____
    Overall appearance (interior)
        Good _____ Fair _____ Poor _____

    Overall appearance (exterior)
        Good _____ Fair _____ Poor _____

    Door operations _____

    Control systems _____

    Noise _____

    Code compliance _____

    Handicapped access _____

    Major repairs necessary _____

    Replacement necessary _____

B1.11 SERVICE SYSTEMS – MECHANICAL/PLUMBING

FAC # _____ FACILITY NAME _____ REPLACEMENT
DATE _____ INSPECTOR _____ VALUE $ _____

A. SYSTEM DESCRIPTION

   (a) Services Available:
       Cold Water _____ Hot Water _____ Acid Waste _____
       Oxygen _____Natural Gas _____ Vacuum _____
       Distilled Water _____ Compressed Air _____ Other _____

   (b) Piping & Fittings
       Cast Iron _____ Copper Tubing _____ Plastic _____
       Steel _____ Glass _____ Other _____

   (c) Water Heaters
       Electric _____ Gas _____ Oil _____

   (d) Drainage
       Storm Drains _____ Sanitary Drainage _____
       Floor Drains _____

   (e) Fixtures
       Water Closets _____ Urinals _____ Lavatories _____
       Showers _____ Kitchen Sinks _____ Slop Sinks _____
       Drinking Fountains _____ Electric Water Coolers _____
       Other _____

   (f) Sprinkler Systems
       Wet _____ Dry _____ Water Storage/Supply _____

   (g) Standpipe Systems
       Wet _____ Dry _____
       Valves _____ Hose Cabinets _____

B. COMPONENT EVALUATION

(a) Condition Rating	(b) Deficiency Report	(c) Priority Rating
1. _____	1. _____	1. _____
2. _____	2. _____	2. _____
3. _____	3. _____	3. _____
4. _____	4. _____	4. _____
5. _____	Total $ _____	

C. MAINTENANCE DEFICIENCY COMMENTS

_____
_____
_____
_____
_____

D. COMPONENT RATING: (   ) x (   ) = _____
                Possible   Condition   Rating
                Rating   Value
                                Multiplier

B1.11 MECHANICAL/PLUMBING INSPECTION CHECKLIST

General Inspection

Occupied spaces:
General appearance
Good _____ Fair _____ Poor _____

Lighting _____
Ventilation _____

Leaks, dripping, running faucets and valves _____
Maintenance history _____
Supply adequacy _____
Sanitation hazards_____
Drain & waste connection _____
Backflow protection _____
Cross connections _____
Fixture quantity _____
Fixture types & conditions _____
Handicapped fixtures _____
Female facilities _____
Metal pipe & fittings corrosion _____
Pipe joints & sealing _____
Hanger supports & clamps _____
Filters _____

Water System

Water pressure adequate _____   Odors, tastes _____
Main cutoff operable _____   Water heating temp. setting _____
Pump condition _____   Insulation condition _____

Sanitary & Storm System

Flow adequate _____   Cleanouts access _____
Floor drains _____   Chemical resistance _____
Gradient _____   On-site disposal system _____

Code Requirements

EPA/local permits _____
Other _____

B1.12 SERVICE SYSTEMS – MECHANICAL/HEATING

FAC # _____ FACILITY NAME _____ REPLACEMENT
DATE _____ INSPECTOR _____ VALUE $ _____

A. SYSTEM DESCRIPTION

(a) Heat Source
Central Plant Steam _____ Central Plant Hot Water _____
Boilers: type _____ size _____
Furnace: type_____ size _____
Heat Pump: type _____ size _____
Burners: gas _____ oil _____

(b) System Type
Steam _____ Hot water _____ Air _____
Electric _____ Solar _____ Other _____
System Capacity _____ (BTUH)

(c) Space Equipment
Radiators _____ Convectors _____ Finned Tube _____
Baseboard _____ 2-Pipe Fan Coil _____ 4-Pipe Fan Coil _____
Unit Ventilators _____ Multizone _____ Radiant Panels _____
Double Duct _____ Terminal Reheat _____
Other _____

(d) Control Type
Pneu _____ Electric _____ Electronic _____ DDC _____
Thermostats (#) _____

(e) Piping
Strainers _____ Basket Type _____ Y-type _____

(f) Traps (steam)
Inverted Bucket _____ F & T _____
Differential Condensate _____
Controlled Disc _____ Radiator _____

B. COMPONENT EVALUATION

(a) Condition Rating (b) Deficiency Report (c) Priority Rating
1. _____   1. _____   1. _____
2. _____   2. _____   2. _____
3. _____   3. _____   3. _____
4. _____   4. _____   4. _____
5. _____   Total $_____

C. MAINTENANCE DEFICIENCY COMMENTS

_____
_____
_____
_____
_____
_____

D. COMPONENT RATING: (   )   x   (   )   =   _____
                          Possible   Condition   Rating
                          Rating   Value
                                        Multiplier

B1.12 MECHANICAL/HEATING INSPECTION CHECKLIST

(See also <u>Means Facilities Maintenance Standards</u>, Chapter 15)

General Inspection
    Building user comments _____
    Lubrication: bearings and moving parts _____
    Rust and corrosion _____
    Motors, fans, drive assemblies, and pumps _____
    Wiring and electrical controls _____
    Thermostats and automatic temperature controls _____
    Thermal insulation and protective coatings _____
    Piping system identification _____
    Burner assemblies _____
    Combustion chambers, smokepipes, and breeching _____
    Electrical heating units _____
    Guards, casings, hangers, supports, platforms, and mounting bolts ____
    Steam and hot water heating equipment _____
    Accessible steam, water, and fuel piping _____
    Traps _____
    Humidifier assemblies and controls _____
    Strainers _____
        (cleaning, maintenance, repairs, and replacement)

Registers _____	Grills _____
Dampers _____	Draft diverters _____
Plenum chambers _____	Supply and return ducts _____
Louvers _____	Fire dampers _____
Air filters:	
Type _____	Replacement schedule _____

System Evaluation
    Heating capacity _____
    Temperature control _____
    Heating:
        Seasonal _____   All year _____
    Noise level _____
    Energy consumption _____
    Air circulation & ventilation _____
    Filtration _____
    Humidity control _____

B1.13 SERVICE SYSTEMS – MECHANICAL/COOLING & VENTILATING

FAC # _____ FACILITY NAME _____ REPLACEMENT
DATE _____ INSPECTOR _____ VALUE $ _____

A. SYSTEM DESCRIPTION

   (a) System
      Type _____ Capacity _____
   (b) Chillers
      Centrifugal _____ Reciprocating _____ Condensers _____
   (c) Cooling Towers
      Type _____ Capacity _____ Condensers _____
   (d) Space Equipment

Direct Expansion - window units _____ thru-the-wall _____
                 single zone _____ all-air multizone _____
                 single zone con. vol. _____ double duct_____
Air/Water -   2-pipe fan coil _____ unit ventilators _____
                 induction _____ 4-pipe fan coil _____
                 terminal reheat _____ self contained _____
                 variable volume _____ var. vol. reheat _____
   (e) Special Systems
      Type _____ Capacity _____
   (f) Control Systems
      Pneu _____ Electric _____ Electronic _____
   (g) Fans: Exhaust _____ Recirculating _____

B. COMPONENT EVALUATION

(a) Condition Rating	(b) Deficiency Report	(c) Priority Rating
1. _____	1. _____	1. _____
2. _____	2. _____	2. _____
3. _____	3. _____	3. _____
4. _____	4. _____	4. _____
5. _____	Total $ _____	

C. MAINTENANCE DEFICIENCY COMMENTS

_____
_____
_____
_____
_____
_____

D. COMPONENT RATING: (_____) x (_____) = _____
                  Possible   Condition   Rating
                  Rating   Value
                                  Multiplier

B1.13 MECHANICAL/COOLING & VENTILATING INSPECTION CHECKLIST

(See Also <u>Means Facilities Maintenance Standards</u>, Chapter 15)

General Inspection

Building user comments _____
Lubrication; bearings and moving parts _____
Rust and corrosion _____
Motors, fans, drive assemblies, and pumps _____
Wiring and electrical controls _____
Temperature and humidity controls _____
Thermal insulation and vapor barriers _____
Guards, casings, hangers, supports, platforms,
    and mounting bolts _____
Piping _____
Solenoid valves _____
Water sprays, weirs, and similar devices _____
Shell-and tube-type condensers _____
Self-contained evaporative condensers _____
Air cooled condensers _____
Compressors _____
Liquid receivers _____
Refrigerant driers, strainers, valves, oil traps,
    and accessories _____
Cleaning, maintenance, repair, and replacement:

Registers _____	Grills _____
Dampers _____	Louvers _____
Bird and insect screens _____	Supply and return ducts _____
Drain pans _____	Coils _____

Air Filters:
    Type _____   Replacement schedule _____

System Evaluation (Cooling)

Cooling capacity _____	Temperature and humidity control _____
Cooling all season _____	Noise level _____
Energy consumption _____	Air circulation & ventilation
Filtration _____	Reliability _____

System Evaluation (Ventilation)

Air velocity _____	Exhaust air systems _____
Bag collection _____	Wet collectors _____
Steam and hot water coils _____	Electrical heating units _____
Fire hazards _____	Fire protective devices _____

B1.14 SERVICE SYSTEMS – ELECTRICAL/SERVICE & DISTRIBUTION

FAC # _____   FACILITY NAME _____   REPLACEMENT
DATE _____   INSPECTOR _____   VALUE $ _____

A. SYSTEM DESCRIPTION

   (a) Service
      Voltage _____   Amperage _____
      Switchgear (type & capacity)_____
      Substation (type & capacity) _____
      Transformers (type & capacity) _____
      Panel (# and capacity)   _____
   (b) Distribution System
      Voltage _____   Amperage _____
      Panelboard (type & capacity _____
      Conduit type _____ Cable Trays _____ Underfloor raceways _____
      Trench duct _____ Bus duct _____ Flat cable _____
      Conductor (alum) _____ Conductor (copper) _____
      Wire (type) _____
      Armored Cable _____ Other _____
   (c) Emergency System
      General or (type & capacity)

B. COMPONENT EVALUATION

(a) Condition Rating	(b) Deficiency Report	(c) Priority Rating
1. _____	1. _____	1. _____
2. _____	2. _____	2. _____
3. _____	3. _____	3. _____
4. _____	4. _____	4. _____
5. _____	Total $ _____	

C. MAINTENANCE DEFICIENCY COMMENTS

_____
_____
_____
_____
_____
_____

D. COMPONENT RATING: (_____)   x   (_____)   =   _____
                       Possible   Condition   Rating
                       Rating   Value
                                       Multiplier

B1.14 ELECTRICAL/SERVICE & DISTRIBUTION INSPECTION CHECKLIST

General Inspection

Safety conditions _____
Service capacity, % used, and age _____
Switchgear capacity, % used, and age _____
Feeder capacity, % used, and age _____
Panel capacity _____
Thermo-scanning: Y ___ N ___   Date _____
Maintenance records available _____
Convenience outlets _____

Exterior Service

Line drawing _____
Feed source:
    Utility/owned: _____   Above/below ground _____
Transformer:
    Transformer tested _____   Transformer arcing or burning _____
    Transformer PCB's _____   Ownership (facility or utility _____

Interior Distribution System

Line drawing _____   Incoming conduit marked _____
Main circuit breaker marked ___ Panel boards, junction boxes covered ___
All wiring in conduit _____   Conduit properly secured _____
Panels marked _____   Panel schedules _____
Missing breakers _____

Emergency Circuits

Emergency generator(s):
    Condition and age _____   Auto start and switchover _____
    Testing schedule _____   Test records available: Y ___ N ___
    Service schedule _____   Service schedule records available: Y ___ N ___
    Circuits appropriate _____   Cooling & exhaust _____
    Fuel storage (capacity) _____

Emergency lighting/power systems:

Battery operation:	Y ___	N ___	Separate power feed:	Y ___	N ___
Exit signs:	Y ___	N ___	Stairways/corridors:	Y ___	N ___
Elevators:	Y ___	N ___	Interior areas:	Y ___	N ___
HVAC:	Y ___	N ___	Exterior:	Y ___	N ___

B1.15 SERVICE SYSTEMS – ELECTRICAL/LIGHTING & POWER

FAC # _____ FACILITY NAME _____ REPLACEMENT
DATE _____ INSPECTOR _____ VALUE $ _____

A. SYSTEM DESCRIPTION

(a) Lighting (lamp type)
Fluor _____ Incand _____ HID _____ Other _____

(b) Emergency Lighting
Battery Pack (#) _____ In Fixture (#)_____
Exit Lights (#) _____ Lights on Emergency Power (#)_____

(c) Motors & Starters
Type & Capacity _____

(d) Receptacles & Switches
Type & Capacity _____

(e) Special
Baseboard Heat _____
Lightning Protection _____
Communication & Alarm _____
Data Systems _____

B. COMPONENT EVALUATION

(a) Condition Rating (b) Deficiency Report (c) Priority Rating
1. _____   1. _____   1. _____
2. _____   2. _____   2. _____
3. _____   3. _____   3. _____
4. _____   4. _____   4. _____
5. _____   Total $ _____

C. MAINTENANCE DEFICIENCY COMMENTS

_____
_____
_____
_____
_____

D. COMPONENT RATING: (_____) x (_____) = _____
Possible   Condition   Rating
Rating   Value
                      Multiplier

B1.15 ELECTRICAL/LIGHTING & POWER INSPECTION CHECKLIST

General Inspection

    Lighting Levels:
        Adequate _____ Excessive _____
        Evenness of distribution _____

    Fixture condition _____
        Flickering of units: Y ___ N ___ Location _____
        Buzzing, humming, or other sounds _____

    Lens condition _____
    Emergency lighting _____
    Exit lighting _____
    Code compliance _____

Wiring, Wall Switches, Lighting Fixtures

    Cover plates in place _____   Junction boxes covered _____
    All wire in conduit _____   Sufficient outlets provided _____
    GFI circuit breakers _____   Grounded wiring _____
    All switches operational _____

    Cleaning, maintenance, repair, and replacement:

_____

B1.16 SAFETY STANDARDS

FAC # _____ FACILITY NAME _____ REPLACEMENT

DATE _____ INSPECTOR _____ VALUE $ _____

A. SYSTEM DESCRIPTION
   (a) Exits
      Stair Construction:concrete _____ steel _____ wood _____.
      Stair Enclosure Rating: none _____ 1 hour _____
      2 hour _____
      Travel Distances _____ Number of Exits _____
   (b) Fire Rating
      Construction Type: I _____ II _____ III _____
      IV _____ V _____ VI_____
      Building Height _____ ft., _____ stories
   (c) Extinguishing Systems
      Portable _____ Standpipe _____ Hose Cabinets _____
      Sprinklers _____ Suppression _____ Other _____
   (d) Detection & Alarm Systems
      Manual Alarm _____ Annunciator _____ Smoke Detectors _____
      Heat Detectors _____ Visual _____ Audible _____
   (e) Lighting Systems
      Exit Signs _____ Exit Lighting _____ Emergency Lighting _____
      Emergency Generator _____ Other Power _____

B. COMPONENT EVALUATION

   (a) Condition Rating (b) Deficiency Report (c) Priority Rating
      1. _____   1. _____   1. _____
      2. _____   2. _____   2. _____
      3. _____   3. _____   3. _____
      4. _____   4. _____   4. _____
      5. _____   Total $_____

C. MAINTENANCE DEFICIENCY COMMENTS

_____
_____
_____
_____
_____

D. COMPONENT RATING: (   ) x (   ) = _____
                Possible   Condition   Rating
                Rating   Value
                          Multiplier

*Building Types:

I	II	III	IV	V	VI
Fire-proof	Fire-resistive	Protected	Slow burning	Combustible	Unprotected
3-4 hour	2 hr. or better	1-2 hr.	1 hr. or better	less than 1 hr.	No rating

B1.16 SAFETY STANDARDS INSPECTION CHECKLIST

General Inspection

Code compliance _____
Maintainability _____
Means of egress _____
Fire ratings _____
Audible & visual device condition _____
Extinguishing systems (see also B1.11 MECHANICAL/PLUMBING):
    Type _____ Condition _____
Lighting system (see also B1.15 ELECTRICAL LIGHTING/POWER):
    Type _____ Condition _____
Handicapped accessibility _____

Exterior Lighting

Adequacy:
    Good _____ Fair _____ Poor _____
Condition _____
Controls (type & location) _____

Fire Alarm Systems

Panel visible: Y _____ N _____   Operational: Y _____ N _____
Pull station condition _____   Detector conditions _____

Stairs and Ramps

Exits marked _____   Hardware operational _____
Tripping hazards _____   Surface conditions _____
Lighting adequate _____   Handrails _____

Building Type Characteristics:

	I	II	III	IV	V	VI
Exterior Walls	Stone, heavy masonry	Brick/stone veneer, heavy masonry back-up	Insul. metal panel, light masonry back-up, maybe bearing wall	Masonry or mas. veneer maybe b.w.	Wood, cement, asbest. or wind-ow wall panels lt. metal/ wood frmg.	Plywood, sheet metal, panels, lt. metal girts, wood frmg.
Structural Framing (Beams columns)	Reinforced concrete, heavy str. steel w/ conc., plaster, F.R. GWB, fire protection	Lt. struc. steel, st. joists, GWB f. prot.		Heavy timber steel/ wood cols.	Wood/lt st. frmg. wd. frmd. bearing walls	Pre-fab. lt steel, wood trusses or built-up rafters, box shell
Floor	Reinf. concrete	R.C., mas. arch. w/ con. fill, heavy battle dk.	Cellular steel or pre-cast concr. slab deck, conc. fill	Heavy timber plank-ing	Frmg: wd lt. met. or st. joist	Sheet metal of plywd. on lt. steel or wood framing
Roof	Reinf. concrete	R.C. or precast concrete		Wd. plank-ing, st,. prec. con. w/con. fill	Deck: plywd. wd. sheath-ing, or protected metal	

Note: Any type may have an element from adjacent types, but should not have a preponderance of elements from a type of higher number (poorer class of construction). (GWB = gypsum wall board)

B1.17A FUNCTIONAL STANDARDS - SUITABILITY & ADAPTABILITY

FAC #_____   FACILITY NAME _____

DATE _____   INSPECTOR _____

A. SYSTEM DESCRIPTION
   (a) Flexible Design Concept _____
   (b) Partitions (Demountable or Rigid) _____
   (c) Specialized Building Type _____
   (d) Flexible Service Systems _____
   (e) Stationary Equipment _____
   (f) Functional Spaces _____
   (g) Working Environment _____
   (h) Circulation and Functional Relationships _____
   (i) Conflicting Uses _____
   (j) Code Conformance _____
   (k) Deferred Maintenance _____

B. COMPONENT EVALUTION
   (a) Condition Rating
       1._____
       2._____
       3._____
       4._____
       5._____

C. COMMENTS:
_____
_____
_____
_____
_____
_____

D. COMPONENT RATING: (   )   x   (   )   =   _____
                         Possible   Condition   Rating
                         Rating   Value
                                           Multiplier

B1.17B FUNCTIONAL STANDARDS – USE CONSIDERATIONS

FAC #_____   FACILITY NAME_____._____

DATE_____   INSPECTOR_____

A. SYSTEM DESCRIPTION

1. **Traditional Values**	Significant role or meaning relative to organization's customs, traditional practices or values.
2. **Historic Values**	Significance to the organization or community for historic associations similar to National Register of Historic places criteria.
3. **Esthetic Value**	Visual qualities and physical relationships with other buildings or the landscape.
4. **Social/Community Values**	Benefits or detriments to location and/or community.
5. **Interim Use**	Facility can be used temporarily for other uses.
6. **Future Land Use**	Conflicting land use with future plans.
7. **Suitability**	Spatial characteristics relative to specific use or is suitable for highly specialized use difficult to replace.
8. **Intangible Values**	Orientation, psychological environment, noise, odors, etc.

B. COMPONENT EVALUATION

(a) Condition Rating

1._____
2._____
3._____
4._____
5._____

C. COMMENTS:

_____

_____

_____

_____

_____

D. COMPONENT RATING: (   ) x (   ) = _____
                    Possible   Condition   Rating
                    Rating   Value
                                  Multiplier

C.1 BUILDING DATA SUMMARY

BUILDING NUMBER	BUILDING NAME	BUILDING USE*	LOCATION/ ADDRESS	OWNERSHIP** OWN/LEA/O-L

*Principal and Special Uses

** Own = Owned
   Lea = Leased
   O-L = Owned/Leased

C.2 BUILDING CONDITION ANALYSIS

1. BUILDING INFORMATION

Bldg _____ Bldg Name _____ Location _____

Date _____ Inspector_____

Year Const, Addn _____

Gross Sq Ft _____ Net Sq Ft _____

2. BUILDING CONDITION ANALYSIS

Building Component	Condition	Repair/Renovation Recommendation
A. Primary Structure		
1. Foundations		
2. Substructure		
3. Superstructure		
4. Exterior Closure		
5. Roofing		
B. Secondary Structure		
6. Partitions & Doors		
7. Walls & Finishes		
8. Floor Finishes		
9. Ceiling Finishes		
C. Service Systems		
10. Conveying		
11. Mechanical: Plumbing		
12. Mechanical: Heating & Ventilating		
13. Mechancial: Cooling		
14. Electrical: Service & Distribution		
15. Electrical: Lighting & Power		
D. Safety Standards		
16. Egress		
17. Fire Ratings		
18. Extinguishing Systems		
19. Detection & Alarms		
20. Emergency Power		
E. Energy Conservation		
21. Source of Energy		
22. HVAC		
23. Lighting		
24. Insulation		
F. Handicapped Access		
25. Circulation		
26. Services		
G. Functional Standards		
27. Adaptability		
28. Use Considerations		

C.3 PROJECT REQUEST FOR REPAIR AND RENOVATION

_____ _____FY
   Location

_____
   Building

1. Project Title _____

2. Priority Number _____

3. Project Description and Justification _____
_____
_____
_____
_____
_____
_____
_____
_____
_____

4. Project Cost Estimate
   Labor $_____
   Materials $_____
   Design Fee $_____
   Owner's Cost $_____
   Contingency $_____

5. Project Schedule

_____
Start Design   Bid   Const Start   Complete

6. Estimate Prepared By: _____

FORM C.4 FIVE YEAR REPAIR AND RENOVATION PROGRAM

Priority Number	Fiscal Year	Project Description	Estimated Cost

INDEX

Management information systems
for facilities planning, 77-79
for maintenance, 106, 108
Moves, planning and supervising,
70

N
National economy, structural changes
in, 4

O
Occupational health and safety
standards, 114
Operating responsibilities, summary
of, 13
Operational plan, 6
Operations and Maintenance
Department, policies and
procedures manual outline, 21
Organization, stages of maturity in,
44
Organizational planning, 19, 20
Organizational structure, for facilities
management, 7-10
Owned properties, property file for,
49

P
Parking control, 119
Performance, monitoring, 23-27
Physical data, for Facilities Audit,
157
Physical development policy, 62,
123-24
Planned maintenance, 144
Preventive maintenance, 83, 144
Priority rankings, for Facilities Audit,
180-81
Priority ratings, in Facilities Audit,
165
Property file, 148
Property management, 9, 11
Property management
departmental functions of, 38
financial impact of, 51
government regulations and, 51
organizational relationships of, 38
policy and procedures outline, 40
space utilization review, 47
specifications for transactions in,
44
strategic, 41-44
Property manager
confidentiality and, 39
policies and procedures involving,
39
qualifications of, 39
relationships of, 39-40
tasks of, 39

R
Real property control file, 48
Real property file
leased properties, 50
owned properties, 49
Regular maintenance, 144
Remodeling, condition ratings and,
163
Renewal and replacement project
estimates, 188
Renovations and modifications, 83
Repair and renovation
five year program for, 174
project request for, 173
Repairs and remodeling, described in
Facilities Audit, 143
Replacement index, calculation of,
191-92
Replacement index method of
estimating, 190-91, 195
Replacement values, and deficiency
repair costs, 163
Resource allocation, 20-22
Results management, 6
Routine maintenance, 144

S
Safety services
accident prevention program and,
115
emergency procedures as part of,
116
function of, 114
occupational health and safety
standards and, 114-15
policies and organizational structure
of, 114
reporting, investigating, and record
keeping for, 115
surveys and inspections for, 115
Scheduling, for Facilities Audit,
155, 157
Schematic design, 65
Security services
coordination with other agencies,
114
crime prevention and, 113
function of, 112
organization of, 112-13
policies and procedures for, 113
Space inventories, 69
Space management and utilization,
68
Space utilization, 126
and allocation, 69-70
Staff performance evaluation, 24-26
Strategic Facilities Development Plan
Facilities Improvement Plan as part
of, 126-29